*A Literary Journal*

Volume Twenty-One Fall 2010
Glendale Community College
Glendale, California

ECLIPSE
A Literary Journal

EDITOR	Bart Edelman
FICTION EDITOR	Michael Ritterbrown
FICTION READERS	Mara Beckett Deirdre Mendoza
	Ara Corbett Chris Pasles
	Denise Ezell Claire Phillips
	Emily Fernandez Piper Rooney
	Rosemary Kwa William Rosenblatt
	Kate Martin Rowe Shant Shahoian
POETRY EDITOR	Bart Edelman
EDITORIAL ASSISTANTS	Elena Grigorian
	Arin Keshishian
BOOK DESIGN	Susan Cisco
COVER DESIGN	Greg Parks
COVER ART	Bill Vuksanovich
	Sisters II, 2007
	Color pencil, 41" x 32.5"
	Koplin Del Rio Gallery
	Culver City, California

Eclipse thanks the Associated Students of Glendale Community College, Stuart Riddle and Melita Bauman Riddle, Kenny Brooks, and the Professional Development Center for their generous grants. We also wish to express our gratitude to Gael and John Davitt, Dawn Lindsay, Larry Serot, Ron Nakasone, Ron Harlan, Kristin Bruno, Hbuk Bayer and Susan Cisco for their support.

Eclipse is a literary journal published annually at Glendale Community College. The editors invite submissions of poetry and fiction. Manuscripts will be returned only if accompanied by a self-addressed, stamped envelope. Sample issues are $8.

Printed by McNaughton and Gunn, Saline, Michigan.

Glendale Community College
1500 North Verdugo Road
Glendale, California 91208
eclipse@glendale.edu

ISSN 1530-5066
ISBN 0-9840883-0-X

In loving memory of Chris McCarthy,
whose gentle nature and grace touched us all
and allowed this journal to flourish.

CONTENTS

Jenny Yang Cropp/Orbit

His wife says he loves you. He thinks
you hung the moon. Seventeen and all you know
is that stars take longer, and what then? You're gone,
off to college when she's off her meds, trying
to time the light so no one sees.
Something always drops from the sky
when you're not looking, and a small mass
hurtles toward Earth, falling down and down
until it meets resistance. After finals and his divorce,
you learn the truth is, she was jealous of you,
or so he says, his hands planted
on your shoulders. That's exactly how
you described it when your father wanted to know
if your teacher ever touched you. You should have
told his wife about the falling, about the leaves
and rain and stones, how mountains let go,
clouds let go, even axils between stems
and branches weaken and release. We fall
by force, attraction, gravity. That's how we meet
in pools of water and piles of leaves. That's how
we love in damp stretches of grass and debris.
You could have told her about the moon,
how it was never meant for him, but something
dropped, and you were new to collision.
What did you know about hanging the moon,
how it escapes its falling, how it moves
away at constant speed?

Jenny Yang Cropp/Dragon in Snow

Made from the language of precision,
stitched by tongue and lip, merging
of vowel and consonant, symbol and object,
mother and father swelling
with love, love, love.
Union, birth, and naming. Now I move
through the world at 35,000 feet,
fly south in winter, mark miles
by the shrinking snow. In the rows
ahead of me a man will brace my body
with his own to keep me from falling.
I will think of my father, feel safe
for the first time, forgive him his sins.

Measure twice and cut once
if you work with wood or stone, but flesh
cuts again and again. My father paints
his life by number. One for red,
two for yellow. When the snow below me
recedes into a dragon billowing smoke,
I know he'll come to find me, legend
in one hand, paints and brushes in the other,
ready to fill the space between
all the lines I've drawn.

Pam Crow/Stone Lesson

I can line up
the right ones,
smooth, flat discs
             but when I throw
                    there is one lone *plash*
     before the bottom—
not like your quick
     twist that sends stones
          stuttering so fast
            they almost speak.

You say it's all in the wrist
but it's not that easy
     being one who lives in the mind
         the body itself matter
         that tends to sink.
I'd be content to kiss
the pebble of bone
beside that wrist,
     be the current that travels
         through your carpal tunnels,
          your metatarsals.

But you arrange your body behind mine,
     breasts to back, arm to arm
         move me in the rhythm of
           my hand's curve, release.
Like this.

Pam Crow/When She Knew

One day the Baby Jesus appeared
　　on their doorstep, unharmed,
　　　　a note taped to his plaster chest.

He had not been stolen, just borrowed—
　　spirited away on a statue vacation.
　　　　An album with photos, brief captions,

followed his journey: Jesus at the Corn Palace,
　　beside Old Faithful, descending a Super Slide,
　　　　his dimpled hands raised in beneficent delight.

She could see a pair of cut-off jeans, a muscled forearm
　　against the door of a red Ford truck, an aqua corner of sky.
　　　　She had just finished wrapping her Thanksgiving

cornucopia and papier-mâché vegetables in newspaper.
　　Instead of unpacking the crèche, the Santa plates,
　　　　she sat among boxes imagining their route

past cornfields, farther than she had ever gone. Time for dinner
　　came and went, her husband in the living room planning
　　　　how this year he would bolt the manger to cement,

affix Baby Jesus to the manger with Gorilla Glue, keep his rifle
　　ready in the garage, damn kids, don't know the meaning of
　　　　private property. While his voice grew louder, calling for her,

she slipped out back in her Dearform slippers, looked out beyond
　　the black-topped road, glazed with frost, into the darkening
　　　　expanse of night sky, the clear and undemanding stars.

Allen C. Fischer/Desire

Looking for someone to blame,
I laid a wreath at the tomb of desire.
No one knew where the weight of sorrow belonged.
October had come apart, failure claimed the latest
peace talks; I felt little need to be reasonable.
What is it about guilt that attracts a crowd?
A trader wouldn't choose me even if the money
were right. Too much wants to happen but won't.
The sidewalks are hustling trash, bars haven't
opened yet, and I am afraid the phone will go dead.
Is this intimacy's breach of promise? If forced to find another
apartment, I'll probably leave town and return to Scranton.
At least, no one remembers me there, no night life either.
A man is measured by the milk run of his daydreams.
No need to read the paper or know about the next
hit on Broadway. No one cares. April waits
like an ice cream cone. Soon short sleeves and
summer tomatoes. Soon air conditioned relief.
Don't they know the Holy Grail was cast in Pittsburgh?
And that desire camps under a fig leaf, passion as
painful as when monks sung it in the ninth century.

Allen C. Fischer/Missing at Birth

No starlit sky signaled my landfall,
nor did lost souls pick up and head for
the nearest clinic. It was a morning like any other.
The papers reported fires, murders, felonies
and continued war in the Middle East.
It's not easy to reconstruct without a chart,
a diary or someone to recollect. My mother
died years ago; my father didn't believe,
not in Christmas or birthdays. His focus was
macro: macroeconomics, macromanagement.
When I was small, foreign policy took him away.

On a beach after a storm, my memory searches
among shells, fish, broken boats, boards and tar balls.
Maybe I was in my room, waking from a nightmare
as everything swarmed, rose up in the dark,
the covers gathering around my neck. Or was it
a neighbor crying, now screaming, perhaps
the specter of a Picasso portrait: eyes pronged,
teeth on edge, the picture pieced together
like a broken dish from a Greek dig.
A surface for mending and make-believe,
what might become. No psychic would know.
The past is pickled in witch's brew.
With happiness missing, no medicine works.

Ellen Wade Beals/Oh, Reader

My life is a series of doors
that don't shut,
cabinets that wonk open
as soon as my back is turned,
exposing the folded paper bags and dog food.

Or, the pantry flaunts its dusty cans,
half-used envelopes of onion soup,
old Bloody Mary mix
while the medicine chest, flapped open,
spills my pills and foibles.
Some days nothing stays shut.

Pesky as the car door that bounces open,
the latch jammed by the seatbelt.
See—nothing retracts perfectly.

Never do I hear the satisfying slam
of the book shutting, the story told.
One plot always bleeds into another
like dandelions taking a field,
necessitating I consult the index
and scroll through menus of memories.

Compartmentalized as the pigeonholes
of an antique secretary.
But the order to things? Tangential—
receipts and pushpins mixed together,
gum wrappers in the pages of an old phone book.
One day it's tuna noodle casserole and
the next a girl's whisper in the library
dwarfs me, hulking as a monument,
shiny and reflective but a little distorted.

Nothing is ever really over.
Now touches then.
It might be glimpsed like a slide
on an overhead projector or
brought into focus under a microscope—
or down and dirty like the last card in poker.
All of it sketchy,
the nasty and beautiful, profane and smudged,

like a gemstone in a Kleenex
or the pink bra strap that slithers out of the drawer
as I write this. Every intimate detail revealed,
explicit as an ashtray,
conspicuous as a cadaver on a slab.
Laid bare.

Bits of me are everywhere.
A mess.
It's as if you've stumbled into my room
while I'm getting undressed.
I'm so embarrassed. Please just back out.

Laura Powers/Persephone's Final Stand

Kept to a house, kept to a marriage,
and embraced by nothing but landscape,
one chill-blue morning, I take off
fleet of foot, over hills swept by snow
crusted hard after a week of ice-clear nights.
I hurry past the polebarn burdened
with last year's grub-ridden firewood,
circle our pond, sucked dry by cattails.
I move downwind of woodsmoke,
the house, the husband,
run for deeper woods, deceived by snow—

—misjudge the sun as it bends
against a tamarack's south side. Winter
sinks fast to spring and it's time
to turn back; yet, in ever-softening snow I
pull still forward; each step plunges me
to the hip, but I shake loose its grip, steady myself
against a run of barbed wire fence that
surrounds our land.

My breath—a rough white tide—startles
a whitetail doe from a copse of hemlock.
Although wasted by winter, she leaps for the fence,
flounders on the wire. She tears, struggles, rips—
her tender doeskin flying—then she gives up, gives in.

But one live roving eye hooks mine in dumb knowing—
a stygian pool of an eye—reflecting darkling chaos.
And so I leave her to be shucked hollow by scavengers.
Leave her to be corrupted into the pure snow.

Richard Hedderman/Advice

There are times when I would say:
just put down your pen, rise
from your desk and just walk away.
Leave the wrack of strewn papers
and the open wings of books.
Leave the ropery of written language,
its infinite treacheries, its diabolical expositions.
Leave Grushenka sulking at dawn
by the banks of the indifferent Volga.
Accept that realism is overrated,
that plot is an elaborate joke. Abandon
literature's dead-ends of grief
and quatrains of the inexplicable.
Instead, build a stone wall, stack firewood,
sweep the stairs, star-gaze. Do anything
but write. Walk, clothed in rags,
into the astonishing world. Walk
into shadow, and the hollows of shadow.
Consider the lost river of your life.
Know that a stroke of lightning
may not be enough.
Shudder with disappointment.
Refuse to say it all. Be alone.
Ignore deadlines. Fish.

Suellen Wedmore/In a Kitchen in Connecticut

—with an apology to Wallace Stevens

I

Among twenty loaves of bread,
The only moving thing
Was the poet's harmonium.

II

I was of three minds
Like the unbraided strands
Of a challah.

III

A recipe whirled like a blackbird's wing.
It was an unreadable speck
In the cadence of exact sound.

IV

A poet and a reader
Are one.
A poet and a reader and a baguette
Are one.

V

I do not know which to prefer,
The precarious music
Of kneaded dough,
Or the transparent eyelids of a beaver.

VI

Winter swallowed the dry birds.
The shadow of an icicle
Crossed to and fro.

The focaccia collapsed in the oven.
Was it old yeast
Or indecipherable hands?

VII

O lithe editors of New York,
Why do you imagine golden loaves?
Do you not see my inkwell
Filled with bright crayon?

VIII

I know the flecked river
And the wilderness of stars.
But I know too
That leavening
Is part of what I know.

IX

When I hurled the chapati
Down the hillside,
It inscribed the dark-blue air.

X

At the sight of poppy seeds
On a thin sheet of paper,
Solitude ripened
Like an Anjou pear.

XI

Enter the ovens of Connecticut
as you might a tramcar.
Once, fear pierced him
In that he mistook a loaf of bread
for the shadow of a blackbird.

XII

The biscuit is rising.
The poet must be writing.

XIII

It was Hartford all afternoon.
The brioche was baking
And it was going to bake.
The scent of yeast lingers
In the cedar limbs.

Mary R. Estrada/Nightingale Hymns

Melancholy penetrates inward,
Framed, subdued through depth;
Reminiscent portraits reveal
Inchoate fragments, apparitions.
Heightened dissonance appears.

Prescient yesterday withdraws,
Its vestiges reach backward
On wings that melt and course
Faster, always faster, and then—
Faint dawn floats end-to-end throughout.

Gazing into the feathery glow
Dazzling shards mark traces,
Races run, long finishes savored
Unhurried essence—
Threatened, burning feverish.

Nameless narratives unfold,
Footprints fade, imprints remain.
Let's profess this space,
Ebullient enigmas fast imbued—
Anecdotal music, nightingale hymns.

S. James Stambaugh/White Boy

The day was nearly over, and that was just fine with me. Trust me, owning a pawn shop ain't no cakewalk, and by the end of the day I was ready to chuck the whole damn thing. Sometimes you just get tired, you know?

All day crackheads, gang-bangers, and petty, thievin' punks had be-bopped in off the street, trying to pawn their worthless, stolen trash. It was a typical Saturday.

I was arguing at the counter with a local crackhead named Lucas when the white guy walked in. I didn't pay any attention to him; a white guy in a polo shirt and jeans is pretty much the least threatening thing I see all day. Know what I mean?

"Now, now I done told you, I got it fo' my birfday," Lucas said, gesturing with jerky, shaking hands at a faceless car stereo he'd brought in. "It's a Sony. Bitch be worth fo' hundred dollars."

"What, they was planning on giving you the face for Christmas?" I wanted to tell him to get the hell out, but you never knew with these guys. A brother who'd steal a car stereo with the detachable face removed may not be smart, but he could be dangerous. "I can't take it without the face."

The white guy was strolling the aisles, stopping to absently strum a guitar or turn the knobs on a stereo. He saw me watching and nodded. I nodded back.

"Yo, listen, you gotta take dis. I need da damn money." He gave a nervous little hop, then added, "You know how it is."

Yeah, I knew how it was, and it almost made me sad. Of course, I squashed that feeling like a bug; I could be sad all damn day if I started that.

"I ain't takin' no stereo that ain't got a face," I told him again. "I can't sell it, and if the police caught me with it I'd be screwed."

"Man, what kind'a brotha are you?" His face was all twisted sideways, reminding me of my beagle when I used words he didn't understand. He didn't understand many; he was a pretty dumb beagle.

"I'm a brother tryin' to make a livin'," I said. "Now why don't you let me be? I got other customers to deal with."

The white boy had ambled up behind Lucas, waiting for him to finish his business.

"Damn, you ain't no kind'a brotha. I ain't comin' in here no mo'."

"You'll be sorely missed."

"I'll show yo' ass sorely missed, nigga-mothafucka."

"Thank you, have a nice day." Sometimes it's almost fun to be polite.

Lucas gave me a "fuck you" glare, grabbed the faceless stereo from the glass counter, and turned and slouched for the door. His pants weren't riding halfway down his ass like I'd almost gotten used to, but all the way down on his upper thigh. It was prison chic.

Sometimes you can understand something and still not *understand*. Know what I mean?

The white guy watched Lucas leave. He was stocky, and though dressed decently he wasn't well-groomed enough to pass for an all-out yuppie. He hadn't shaved for at least a day, but was clean and normal nonetheless. I'd guess him to be about twenty-five. He wore his polo shirt outside his pants, but I could see the wrinkles around the bottom where it had been tucked in. The door closed in Lucas' wake with a jingle, and the white guy turned back to me.

"That looked like fun," he said with a smile.

"Yeah, well, it ain't as much fun as it looks," I said. "What can I do you for?"

"Well, I'm afraid your day isn't getting any better," he said, sort'a half smiling.

He reached for his back, and even though I knew what he was doing my mind wouldn't grasp it. I mean, maybe it was because he was white and well dressed, or whatever, but I wasn't prepared like I might have been. I prepare for this shit like a reflex, but not this time. He came up with a gun, a Heckler & Koch USP-45.

For those of you who don't know, that's a big bastard of a gun. It'll blow a hole in a brother you could toss a cat through.

"I've got a gun," he said, just like that, smiling. You'd think he just pulled a rabbit from a hat.

"Okay. . ." I was trying to be cool, but I have to admit, I was a little freaked. I hadn't seen this coming.

Like most pawn shop owners, I'm a paranoid. Get robbed a few-dozen times and you get that way. Anyhow, I've got guns all over the place; stashed behind the counter, hidden beneath the register. I've got guns coming out my ears.

"Go lock the front door," he said.

I was staring him right back in the eyes, not trying to be bad or nothing; I was just trying to read him. You get robbed by one of the cracked-out brothers in this neighborhood and they tell you to lock the front door, you know you're going to die. But this guy, it was hard to tell. I just don't think of white boys in blue polos as killers.

He didn't have it in the eyes, either. There wasn't that nervous, spastic twitch that a brother gets when he's jonesin' for a pipe, and they weren't the dead eyes of a real killer-type killer.

He was just a white boy in a blue polo, with a gun.

"Go lock the door," he said again. "Now."

I nodded, took the keys from my belt, and walked around the end of the counter. The muzzle of his pistol followed me. I could almost feel it on the back of my neck. I didn't feel like I was going to die, but I didn't feel like I was going to live, either.

I turned the key in the lock and the heavy bar fell with a "clank." I paused for a second then, a little frozen. The lock had never sounded quite like *that* before. I should'a tried to rush out the door, that's what I should'a done, but I was so nervous I just did what I was told like a dumb-ass.

"Turn the sign around."

I nodded, then turned the "Open/Closed" sign around. Had it been earlier in the day I might have hoped that would draw suspicion, but it was nearly closing time anyway and I tended to leave a little early on slow days. Nobody would think a thing about it.

I turned to look at him, but all I saw was the hole at the end of his pistol. It was like a tunnel, a long, dark bitch of a tunnel.

He jerked with his head for me to come back to the counter, which made me feel a little better. That was, after all, where my guns were. I decided then that I should assume the worst; White Boy aimed to kill me, and given the chance I was going to pop a cap in his polo-wearing ass.

I came back around the counter like he motioned me to do, then opened the register when he nodded at it. The butt of a Makarov 9mm Short was sticking out from beneath the counter near the lower-right corner of the register. I tried not to look at it. His pistol was still aimed at my face so pulling the Mak wasn't an option. Not yet, anyhow.

The register had an alarm system that was activated if the last bill was removed from the left-hand slot where the twenties were stacked. When the last bill was removed the metal arm would contact the metal base of the tray, completing a circuit and sending a silent alarm. I removed all the bills from the tray and stuffed them into a paper bag.

"All of it," he commanded.

I lifted the tray and removed a fifty and a hundred, putting them in the bag as well. I folded the top of the bag and looked at him.

White Boy was looking over my shoulder at the rack of rifles that lined the wall behind. He didn't seem to be in any hurry to leave.

"Get me that. . ." he began.

The phone rang.

I looked at White Boy and he nodded, then drew back the hammer on his pistol—a not-so-subtle threat. I stared for a second at that big hole, then reached for the receiver.

"Dixon Street Pawn," I said, trying to sound calm.

"This is Beverly with Robb Alarm. We have a register alarm at your business going off. Is everything all right?"

"Damn, I done worked all day. I don't wanna stop at no store. Why can't you get the eggs when you out?" I looked at White Boy and gave an irritated shake of my head.

He sort of smiled, like he understood. He was pretty empathetic for a guy with a gun.

"We'll consider that a confirmation that the alarm is legitimate. Police will be dispatched immediately." The lady's voice was pinched and dispassionate. Either she'd done this shit a million times and was bored, or she was annoyed with me for getting robbed and disturbing her afternoon. "This call is now being monitored. How many suspects are there?"

"What you mean you ain't got no money? I gave you money this mornin' and you can't buy one dozen eggs?"

"Is that one man, sir, or a dozen men?"

"You can't buy one?"

I was watching White Boy as I spoke and he narrowed his eyes impatiently, then tapped at his watch with the snout of the gun. I shrugged and threw him a pained expression.

"Does the suspect have a gun, sir?"

Suspect, hell! I didn't *suspect* him of nothing; he was doing it.

"What'choo think? Yeah, I can pick up some damn eggs. Is there anything else?"

"Just try to stay on the line, sir. Police should be there any minute."

White Boy rapped on the glass counter with his knuckles, then made big show of staring down the slide at the middle of my forehead.

"I gotta go. I got a customer."

"Sir, are you okay?"

White Boy gave a little cough, and I nodded.

"Yeah, I told you I'll stop at the damn store. Now I gotta go."

I hung up the phone and looked at White Boy, feeling a funny kind of good, like I'd just pulled something off.

"That your wife?" he asked.

"No, I ain't got no wife. That was my momma."

"Kind'a rough on your momma, aren't you?"

"You don't know my momma."

White Boy thumbed the safety on his pistol and the hammer dropped back to the safe position.

Given the standard police response time, usually about four or five minutes, I figured on being either alone or dead by the time they arrived. I badly wanted to hurry, get him what he wanted and get him out, but White Boy didn't seem terribly interested in leaving. He acted like he had all the time in the world, which he probably thought he did. All I knew is I wanted him out before the police got there. I didn't want to be no hostage.

White Boy's attention had turned again to the rifles behind the counter. Most of them were garbage; rusted old shotguns, hunting rifles with cheap scopes, that kind of shit. But there were a few decent ones, too.

Beneath the rack was a stack of gun bags, and alongside the bags was a pile of other accessories like slings, cleaning kits, and extra magazines.

"Give me one of them bags," he said, pointing beneath the rifle rack with the muzzle of the pistol.

"Why don't you let me leave, then you take what you want?" I asked, not because I really thought he'd go for it but because I really, really didn't want to turn my back to him.

"Why don't you shut the fuck up and get me one of them bags?"

I backed away from him, not turning around, then reached the wall and kneeled and picked up one of the gun bags. I walked cautiously back to the counter and placed the bag on the glass.

"I want guns and am. . ." he began, then looked back to the rack on the wall behind me. "That AR-15. Get me that."

There were three AR-15s on the rack so I selected one at random and brought it to the counter, setting it down.

"You got ammo for that?"

"Yeah," I said.

Then he did the strangest, dumbest thing. He sat his pistol down on the counter and picked up the rifle. I could tell he was ex-military by the way he brought the rifle up and pulled the bolt back and checked the chamber. He was ex-military, for sure, but he weren't no robber. I almost laughed out loud as my hand darted for the Mak.

I brought the pistol up and pulled the hammer back in one motion. The rifle was still raised and he peered over it, first at me then at the pistol aimed at his face.

I was almost shaking from. . . I don't know—triumph? I wasn't even going to have to shoot the dumb son of a bitch. The police would come and I'd turn him over, and that would be that.

White Boy pressed the bolt release on the AR-15 and the bolt slammed home with a loud crack that made me jump just a little. I backed away a step just to make sure there was no way he could hit me with it. He just stood there looking at me without the slightest bit of alarm.

Then he smiled, and his hand started toward the pistol he'd left on the counter.

"Don't do it, asshole," I said, trying to sound real threatening. "Don't make me shoot yo' dumb ass."

His smile only widened as his hand continued toward the gun.

"I mean it! I'll shoot you in the fuckin' face!" My hand was shaking as I stared down the barrel at him. Something seemed to creep into his expression. I don't know what it was, but it wasn't fear. I had hoped for fear.

Over his shoulder I saw the first police car pull into the parking lot, then saw another policeman watching through the corner of the big plate-glass window. His view was obstructed by a row of shelves stacked with tool boxes and rusty hammers and wrenches. I wondered how long he had been there.

The wall behind the counter was mirrored for security, and I saw the arrival of the police register in White Boy's eyes.

"Cops," he said. His hand had halted momentarily, but then continued toward his pistol. I began to take up the slack on the Makarov's trigger.

"Don't!" I shouted, but he ignored me and made a sudden grab for his pistol. I pulled the trigger.

The hammer fell with a heavy click.

Shit. . .

"Try again," White Boy said with a smile that seemed oddly sympathetic. His pistol was once more pointed at my face. "I'm serious, try again."

He swung the barrel of his pistol away from my face, and I immediately began pulling the trigger.

Clack! Clack! Clack! Clack!

It was unbelievable. For the first time I truly regretted being such a cheap bastard. The Makarov, like most of the guns I had stashed behind the counter, had been taken in on pawn. I'd never even fired it. It was close enough to being worthless that I didn't bother trying to sell it, instead choosing to make it a part of my personal armory. And the bitch didn't work.

"That's gotta be a disappointment," White Boy said. Funny thing was, *he* seemed more disappointed than me.

"Shit yeah it's disappointing!" I said, completely freaked and not thinking much.

By now the cops weren't even trying to pretend they weren't there. Black and whites stood bumper to bumper out front, lights all flashing and throwing funny red and blue splashes around my shop. Behind the cruisers were cops, maybe a dozen, pointing a variety of barrels at White Boy.

White Boy was still pointing his pistol at my head, but I could see his eyes flick to the mirror occasionally. He knew what was going down out there. He had to know his options, and they all sucked.

"Man," I started, "I don't know what you was plannin', but it ain't workin' out. You ain't gonna get out of this."

He smiled a little, but seemed uncomfortable, maybe a little nervous. Finally. He couldn't seem to stand still, shifting his weight from one leg to the other.

White Boy's finally comin' undone, I thought, though I knew that wasn't necessarily a good thing.

"I'm gettin' out of it. Don't you. . ."

The phone rang, interrupting him. We both looked at it for a few seconds, then he nodded.

I picked up the phone.

"Yeah?" I said.

"This is Captain Donovan of the Middleburg Police Department. Is this Nathanial Stokes?" That's my name: Nathanial Stokes. My friends call me Nate.

"Yeah," I said.

White Boy was watching me down the barrel of his pistol, seeming more nervous by the second. He was practically dancing in front of the counter.

"Is everything all right, Mr. Stokes?"

"What the hell you think?" I asked. "Some crazy-assed white boy got a gun pointed at my head. How you doin'?" Cops ask the dumbest damn questions sometimes.

"Now just stay calm, we're going to get you out of this. Can we speak to the, ahhh. . . this white boy, Mr. Stokes?"

"They wanna talk to you," I said to White Boy.

He shook his head.

"He said no," I told the cop.

"Okay. Okay. Ummm. . . tell him we have the place surrounded, and if he gives up we'll see that he is treated fairly."

"Yo," I said to White Boy, "they say you're surrounded and if you give up everything'll be cool."

White Boy shook his head, still dancing.

"He says no," I said into the phone.

"Yes, Mr. Stokes," the cop said, "we saw him shake his head. What does he want, Mr. Stokes? Ask him if he has any demands."

"They wanna know if you got any demands," I said to White Boy. "They wanna know what you want."

"I wanna piss, is what I want," White Boy said. "You got a bathroom in this place?"

I just looked at him, all stupid-faced. *He's gotta piss, Christ. . .*

"Yeah, I got a bathroom," I said, finally.

"Good, hang up the phone and show me."

Now, I didn't want to go to the bathroom with White Boy. I mean, despite all his dancing, which I had thought meant he was nervous, I didn't really believe he had to piss. I thought he was going to take me in the back and waste me. I think I almost turned white as him.

"Now," he said.

"White Boy's gotta go pee," I said to the cop.

"Don't hang. . ." the voice on the other end started, but I hung up before he finished.

I led White Boy into the back where we stored all the stuff waiting to be picked up by borrowers. Most of it would end up being for sale.

I took him to the bathroom and nodded at the door when we

reached it.

"You've gotta come, too," he said.

Damn. . .

The bathroom is tiny; it's not meant to be for the public. It's just a toilet, a sink, and a door. That's it. But White Boy made me squeeze in there with him.

He scooted around between the wall and the toilet so he could keep his gun on me while he pissed.

The phone rang constantly out front. The bathroom smelled like piss. I was sweating. White Boy wasn't.

White Boy had a hard time getting his zipper down with only one hand, since the other was holding that big-ass pistol. It was kind of funny, and when that mixed with the relief of seeing he really did have to piss I almost laughed.

He finally got his zipper down and I stared at the wall while he peed.

When he was done, he motioned me out of the bathroom.

"Feel better?" I asked, kind of smart-assed.

"Feel lighter," he said.

Now, what do you think happened next? Damned if listening to him piss didn't make me have to go, too.

"I kind'a gotta go, too," I said. White Boy rolled his eyes and nodded.

"Fine," he said.

We had to jockey around real close to change positions, banging into each other and stepping on each other's feet. I probably could of taken the gun away from him, since we were so close, but I didn't want it to go off accidentally. Weird thing is, I remember I was thinking about how loud it would be in that tiny bathroom more than I was worried about getting shot.

As I relieved myself White Boy started whistling that damn Andy Griffith tune. I hate whistling. I hate Andy Griffith, for that matter, too.

When I was done he made me lead him back out front. I didn't understand that; out there he had all them damn guns pointing at him. He walked around to where he was before, on the customer side of the counter. I went back to where I was on the other side.

The phone was still ringing and he picked it up with his free hand, pistol pointed at my face again.

"Sorry, gave at the office," he said into the receiver, then laid it down on the counter and pushed the hang-up button.

He looked around for a moment, for the first time seeming unsure of himself. White Boy didn't have any options, and he had to know it. Having that gun pointed at my head was the only thing keeping him alive.

His eyes settled on the AR-15.

"Load that," he said.

"Man, what you think you're gonna do with that?" I asked. "There's a billion cops out there."

"Just load it."

I got a magazine from the stack below the rifle rack, then knelt down to where the ammo was kept below the counter. His gun stayed on me the whole time.

Next to the stacks of cardboard ammo boxes was another one of my stashed pistols; a government-issue .45. White Boy couldn't see my hands. I reached for the gun. The pistol was what we called "cocked and locked," meaning the hammer was back but the safety was on.

I took it by the butt and switched the safety off with my thumb. I hesitated.

"Come on," White Boy said. "Let's do this thing."

I don't know why, but I put the gun back down. Maybe I was just scared to try to use it, since he had the drop on me. But I don't think that's it. I don't know what it was, but I don't think that was it.

I came up with the ammo and White Boy nodded at the rifle.

"Load it."

I started loading the cartridges into the magazine as red and blue light continued to flash through my shop. I expected the SWAT team to come bursting in with machine guns and napalm any second.

"You wanna hear something funny?" White boy asked, out of no-where.

I just looked at him. I weren't in the mood for jokes. Finally, I nod-ded, and said, "Sure."

He smirked, but it weren't a happy smirk.

"I'm a nice guy. Ain't that a hoot? I've never hurt anybody."

I just looked at him. He seemed suddenly sad, like maybe he was rethinking this whole thing. I didn't know what to say.

"Nobody knows that," he continued, "but I'm really a nice guy." He relaxed his grip on the pistol just a little and I started to think maybe I was gonna get out of this.

"You look like a nice guy," I said. "Why you doin' this?"

"I've got issues," he said, giving me a weak smile.

"We all got issues, man," I said. That seemed to break the spell, because his face became hard again. I should have said something else, but I don't know what.

"Maybe my daddy didn't hug me enough," he said, his voice all business again. "Now load the fuckin' gun."

I finished loading the magazine and looked up at him.

"Load it," he said.

I stuck the loaded magazine into the rifle and, again, looked at White Boy.

"I said load it."

Careful to point it at the wall, I cradled the rifle in my left arm and pulled back and released the charging handle. I set the loaded rifle back on the counter.

White Boy stood there for a long time, at least a minute. He would look at me, then the rifle, and then the mirror.

"You're not married?" he asked. That hardness was out of his voice again.

"No."

"You should be. Kids?"

"Two sons. One's in college. The other's still in high school."

I started thinking things had taken a positive turn. Again. I saw that movie, *Silence of the Lambs*, and it said if he saw me as a person I'd be harder to kill. Of course, that was Hollywood, and in Hollywood white boys in polo shirts don't go around robbing black men to begin with.

"How 'bout you?" I asked.

He ignored my question, switching the pistol to his left hand and reaching for the AR-15 instead. He looked down real quick to check the safety, which was off, then pointed it at my chest.

"How 'bout you, man?" I asked. "You married? Any kids?"

"I bet you're a good dad," he said, ignoring my question. "You a good dad?"

"I try to be. But what about you?"

"Well, you be a good dad, then."

White Boy laid the pistol on the counter and took the rifle in both hands, still pointing it at my chest. He checked the mirror and then looked back at me.

The cops didn't seem to be doing anything new. They were still hunkered down behind their cruisers, pointing their guns. Maybe they just figured on waiting him out, or maybe they were just confused. Either way, they weren't doing nothing.

"You'll be a good dad?" he asked again, his voice almost cracking. I could see tears welling up in his eyes and he looked suddenly tired.

"Yeah, man, I'll be a good dad."

I knew what was going on now. I knew what he was doing and felt the biggest sad I ever felt. At that moment I thought I knew White Boy better than anyone alive, and that pretty much explained everything.

"You do that," he said, and checked the mirror for the last time.

"You don't have to. . ."

"Just duck," he said, cutting me off.

I stood there.

"I said 'duck.'"

I shook my head, not moving. I didn't want this to happen.

He looked at me for a long time, seeming uncertain. His face got all soft and he looked for a second like he might cry. But that was only for a second, and then his face hardened again and his eyes narrowed.

White Boy shook his head.

"Your call," he said, his voice flat, then spun around.

I ducked; I'm not a fool.

I heard maybe three shots from White Boy's rifle before the plate-glass windows exploded in a massive volley from the cops. I cowered there below the register as the firing continued and bloody chunks of White Boy were flung on the mirror. The floor seemed to rumble, but that was probably just me shaking.

Then the firing stopped. I didn't move, other than my shaking, until I heard the rush of feet and shouting. I was just glad to be alive and thankful I didn't piss myself; I'd suffered enough indignity for one day.

I slowly rose. The cops were swarming through the shattered window, guns still pointed at the perforated white boy. I couldn't look at him. I didn't need to see that. I just stood there watching the cops storm in like they were hitting the beach at Normandy.

A cop broke away from the pack circling White Boy and came over to me.

"You okay, Mr. Stokes?"

"What you think?" I didn't feel okay. I felt nothing like okay. What kind of dumb-assed question was that?

"Is that the suspect's gun?" he asked, nodding at the pistol on the counter.

I nodded and the cop picked up the pistol and ejected the magazine. He looked at it, confused, then pulled the slide back and checked the chamber.

"It's not loaded," he said, surprised.

I shook my head and turned away. As far as I was concerned, that was the least surprising thing to happen all day.

Jackie Bartley/The Politics of Sewing

On every pattern packet, directions in English
and in French, a thin, black line the only hint
of ocean separating the two. France, hub
of the fashion world where I had always imagined
myself twinned, another Jacqueline scanning
her packet for fabric suggestions and notions,
checking her size against the measurements.
Taller, more graceful than I. Her consonants
finer, a crisp flutter of wings or stones
skipped over water. Vowels less guttural
and tinged with melody.

Who took her degree from a university
in Paris—nights in smoky cafés, sunrise
on the Seine. Sewed her own tops,
skirts, and slacks. Made flannel shirts
for lovers, in the arms of whom
she nestled through *Jules et Jim*,
La Chinoise, Le charme discret de la bourgeoisie.
Once, in the seventies, for her husband, a green
polyester leisure suit they laugh at now.

If they're together.
If they survived the lean, anticipatory years
before waking in the middle of their lives,
broken affairs, jobs not quite
what they'd expected, a child to raise.
For whom she sewed jumpsuits with
animal appliqués. Who's grown now,
moved light years away, weekends
passing without a visit. Holidays that slip
by quick as a long, flat seam
through a machine.

Till one night,
she's on her knees sorting the ancient fabrics.
Tossing the knits, fingering the flannels,
savoring the silk scraps from a time
when she thought she understood love.

How different can sitting without speaking be
in any language? Sundays on their patio:
chamomile, alyssum in the air, ivy tangling
the base of a stone birdbath. Giant cups of coffee
in their hands, matching robes made
from a pattern labeled *facile*.

Glad to be sewing without the old
regard for economy. Enough to take pleasure
in the task. She's seen the prices on her packet
for Canada, USA, New Zealand, imagined
her counterparts in these countries
attending to the ritual of purchase and layout,
cut and piece. For her, the political remains
private, a simple satisfaction of needle
piercing warp and weft, joining
one small flag of cloth to another.

Ellen Chavez Kelley/Occupation

You were the lumber,
you were the boards
stacked on forklifts
two by four.

You were the log
stripped, delivered,
you were the shipment
milled down river.

You were timber's
stump, the trunk.
You were the woodsman's
chop, the thunk

of sumpter's step
on spruce and pine,
the sap, the twisted
disc. The grind.

Barker, broker,
business trip,
you were the trout,
hook in your lip.

You were the bars,
deals and drinks,
pocket keys, their
icy clink.

You were the father
stretched on a rack,
brackened beast
with shattered back.

You were the keeper,
gate and guard,
you were the sawdust
heaped in the yard:

father, woodsman
keeper, guard,
you were the sawdust
heaped in the yard.

Christopher Buckley/Meditation on the Edge of Drought Above La Purisima Mission, Lompoc, Easter 2008

In the shade of conifers, white streaks of shooting stars,
Star of Bethlehems, trailside, glowing on slender stalks—

and wild peonies, red as meat, hanging over like
the head of Jesus on the cross. . . violet phlox, lupine,

Chinese houses, and oxalis and owl's clover, even
fiddlehead from the spare week of winter rain,

all called forth into the light. But now the water's
gone and the politicians are holding back everything

else—there is nothing new. Only this warbler
on the top-most twig of scrub oak continues sending

his desires to the sky. *Lachryma Christi*, it is late—
I'm trying not to waste what I have left of my life.

Sandra Kohler/August is Autumn

i.

The porch, dawn, fog. My birthday.
It will be hot, it will be close, it will be
summer: August. Last night for the first
time this year, during evening's thunderstorm,
heavy straight rain like ropes, the blackbird
stream over the east, scattered, storm-tossed,
numberless, vanishing.
It's started, the August migration,
restless announcement.

My sister's birthday and
mine bracket a month: August.
Bookends for a span in which
summer turns autumn.

ii.

The news comes suddenly: an old friend,
sister poet, has been in a coma for a week
and died yesterday; the funeral's today. I'll drive
the three hours there, hoping her sons
will read her poems, give her a poet's rites.
On the phone this morning my sister says
she hopes the funeral isn't too sad for me.
But to go to a funeral without being sad
would seem a little death. For some of us
the only sorrow we recognize in another
is one of our own. Protect me from other
things, please, semis and drunk drivers,
my own stupidity and carelessness,
blind spots.

iii.

Last night dreaming took all
my energy, a world I could create and
not comprehend: a jet plane with
my sister piloting it lands in a cornfield
on the island here, I watch it come down,
it just misses grazing a barn, I don't know
why she's there, why we're meeting, how
she comes to be flying this craft.

People suffering attacks of vertigo,
we're told, sometimes throw themselves
down on the ground to stop the sensation
of movement. It's fascinating, scary:
our desperate self-harming attempts
to change the unbearable perceptions
we're experiencing. We're both
doing this, my sister and me:
she in her wishes for me;
me, rejecting them.

iv.

Yesterday morning a white bird—
young heron or egret—at the river,
senses my watching presence, flies
into trees. I feel as small a part of
the universe as the dead chipmunk
smeared on the road, the skinny
garter snake crossing it, the tiny
yellow stars of Jerusalem artichoke
blooming on its verge. On the walk
back, there's a great blue heron on
the tail of what my friend Sabrina's

named the driftwood dragon.
Goldfinch come to the porch feeder
this August day, the finch that were
supposed to leave in June. Now a bee
drinks nectar. I feel some shift in
my life I can't name. It's time
to draw the curtains against
the hot August day.

v.

My sister's birthday.
The sky pure gray overcast,
strangely featureless, unwritten.
But the breeze: this morning
along the river everyone spoke of it,
the breeze is today's news, today's
gift: pleasure, renewal, release from
summer's oppression. A skein of
geese flies past, a scatter of
blackbirds. My poet friend's sons
read her poems, celebrate her
courage at walking into a dark wood,
exploring its deep pools, risking a
plunge into its chasms. In my garden,
in the renewing breeze, insect trill
and buzz, morning's undercurrent.
A flurry of black forms flit into
the mulberry. The red dogwood,
planted years ago in memory
of another friend, is reddening.

Sandra Kohler/Daybreak

The sun brilliant warm wakes
me floods our bed where last
night to our surprise the dance
the game we make sex have love
come to culmination. As all things
come, are coming or not, fail to,
fall by the wayside, why side?
The way itself is sighed, sad,
mourned, turned to a state not
way but weight. But not today,
not last night, not us, not now
this morning moment this flood
of sun rich dark liquid warming
as last night's climax I didn't
miss but as it passed missed it
wanted it to last wanted to stay
to be the way my body sang
and hung suspended
—a web a mesh of
pleasure that doesn't
end a flush rush
lasting
not rushing
past,
passed.

Chris McCarthy/Rinker

*In the Irish the dream gene is dominant, recessive, monstrous,
and once an idea like that takes hold all you can do is strap
yourself in and fly.*

—Rinker Buck

Monks robed like loose-finned fish
Circled when we danced with the girls
Of St. Elizabeth's. Their black habits swished
A quiet warning. Rinker, always with the best girl,
Did a little trudge on the dance floor, fists pumping
Like mechanical pistons.

That summer, he and his brother
Flew across country in
A hand-built Piper Cub. I imagined
Their tiny engine gasping
In papery air over the Rockies.
I saw those fists fighting the levers to maintain
Altitude. He was a hero when he came home,
Fourteen and the youngest boy to fly.

Rinker started a Pilots Club in school.
He talked straight past me,
About lift and wind and apogee. I waited
For the deliverance of flight,
Promised in the small blue manual;
My eyes were too damaged to try to fly.

Years later, I read his book.
I couldn't not look for my name,
Hoping to be even a footnote,
Too small a figure
To be seen from any kind of height.

The Irish do two things well:
We dream, and we hold unreasonable grudges.
If I saw him, if we met as two men standing at a bar,
I would tell him that I think of him every time I dance.

Chris McCarthy/Advice for the Lighthouse Keeper's Daughter

Put a candle in the window.
This is, perhaps, how he will come to you,
lost and in need of care.

Set an extra plate at the table.
If he is unsure,
it will make him feel welcome.

If he has come from the sea,
give him dry wool.
Feed him fish that watched
from the bay.

Sing so he won't hear
the wind-driven waves,
the cracking of timber.

Lay him in a bed
so full of promise
he will never leave.

Think of his hands,
his rough cheek.
Keep a record
of the empty days.

Do these things
And he will surely come.
Set an extra plate
at the table. Prepare the fish.
Put a candle in the window.

Susana H. Case/BEECHWOOD 4-5789

Twelve months old with a boxful of Motown 45s
and an imaginary boyfriend named Randall. I decide he writes novels
and looks like Clark Kent in the Lois Lane DC Comics series
(though can't fly to save his life.) He wears black—jeans
like mine, but without the bottom fringe I pull through each new pair
before I Clorox them to wash out the color, which makes them cool. I lie
in bed for hours, one hand rubbing my breasts, rehearsing
Randall taking off my cat's-eye glasses to French kiss me
—after he tells me he never realized how beautiful I am. A page
from *True Romance*. Having to remove my glasses to be beautiful
makes perfect sense, a fast path to fabulousness. What's best,
he lives right here in what my local paper calls the City of Aspiration.
I aspire to overwhelm him with my authentic sexual self,
though I'm still vague about the details.

One day, my friends and I are sitting around my room, the Marvelettes
on the turntable, as we debate whether we could ever telephone a boy.
Laughing at the idea, I grab my pink Princess and dial BE 4-5789.
A guy answers with a voice like the background fabric of the paintings
sold at the art fair on Saturdays three streets down. *Wait,*
my wrong number says, when it looks like I'm going to do a quick fade,
I believe in fate, don't you? His imaginary girlfriend he calls me.
Meet me at Eddie's, he asks, all sweet with suggestion. I've told him
where I live and that's the nearest ice cream place.

Then, Lizzie and Christine, miming a slow dance, do a dip back
as I slam down the phone, throw myself on the floor,
laughing so hard I hurt. When I dial the number three days later
—after an imaginary fight with Randall—it rings and rings.

Peter Borrebach/Meteorologist's Song

Cool, you are there
in the tidal pool,
green-kneed, wading the brack—
what passes you by?

The pantomime of emergency lights
become a wail,
siren the waterspout,
siren the gaps in the clouds,
the sky's ice before it thaws—
what will you siren of me?

Am I the cracked arc
between two winnowed clouds?

The corduroy bands of rain
brown with twilight,
the wind in all directions?

O dry season's dust-fire,
lick of salt,

ash in the mortar
of a weathervane's brick foundation,

catch and vessel,
lightning rod,

am I the smogless wind?

Peter Borrebach/Song for the Delayed Harvest

We have form.
We have a bathtub stained blue.

We have content.
We have a white shoe
sojourning the center,
buoyant with artifice.

We have this body,
hunched against an open door.

A torn plastic blind slaps the screened window,
knocks a dead fly from the sill.

Three spent matches
accent a dented can on the floor.

Mice in the oven scratch a mild cacophony.
We're killing the children but not the parents.

In the corner, a coconut shell
isolates a puddle of urine.

We have a card every year in August,
no reply. Thanks, sorry.

We have a candle
on the edge of ferocity.

We have process.
We have eyes in the sink.
Blue eyes.
An unchecked remainder.

E. Louise Beach/Florida

All things flourish:
penis fronds unfold, and nectar oozes
crimson. In the glades, snakes hide
under muck and shade. Alligators
snap. Vivid incandescence of ibis,
white light against Viscaya, skitter
of lizards—the wild thriving troubles
us. Banyan cancer and spreading
mangrove threaten our sense of balance.
We peel from the car and walk the beach,
eyes shielded by caps and glasses, ankles
washed by infant waves. A crab bites,
and I slip on bright metastases of stone.
"Too old to play in the ocean," you advise.
Because of the heat, you refuse
to wait as I search the still-wet sand
for shells. We sip our evening drink
while pelicans glide and dive. Our place
gives on the sea, but we do not swim.

David Hovhannisyan/Doors

Abstract reality is verity,
preserving themes which passionately fight,
and circulate perverse polarity.

Benighted twilight offers clarity,
amending peace inferior to sight;
abstract reality is verity.

A melody of silent parity
reveals the vacancy that shuts the night,
and circulates perverse polarity.

Complete arrangements seek temerity,
maneuvering a reverent delight;
abstract reality is verity.

The threshold calculates austerity,
sedating sapience to rouse our spite,
and circulate perverse polarity.

Unbiased doors perceive sincerity
to guide humanity along the rite;
abstract reality is verity,
and circulates perverse polarity.

Phillip Gardner/There's Someone's Shadow in this One

For two hours, Tess Killingsworth and Karen Russell sat in Karen's minivan outside their father's vacant house drinking Bombay Sapphire Gin from giant Styrofoam cups. The gin was cold. They'd kept it on ice inside the cooler along with the tonic and lime slices during the five-hour drive from Atlanta. Now the two women held their cups before them like resolute beggars and stared at the empty house. After a time, their conversation, which had rested for a stretch, lurched forward again.

"I thought you'd had the power disconnected," Karen said.

"I thought so, too," Tess said.

"Wasn't dark when we parked. It got dark in like five minutes. Has the porch light been on all this time?" Karen thought her sister was considering the question.

"Yoooo Liiiite up my liiiife." Tess lifted her cup and searched for the melody.

"That's, ah, ah—. Who the hell sang that?"

"Mama sang that, remember?"

"Debbie Boone, that's who recorded that. Debbie Boone." Karen wagged her head from side to side like it was sad news. "Name like that? I'd have been a heroin addict."

"At the beach that summer. Why the hell did Mama resurrect that piece of shit song? It was ancient twenty years ago."

"It was like her theme song all summer."

"We both could have used some good heroin that summer." Tess looked at her older sister.

"We were too busy smoking pot." The two drank. "A looong, looong time-agooo." Karen was no singer either.

"That's not Debbie Boone. That's *American*. . . shit. *Pie*. Pie shit," Tess said. The dull weight of their words sank into silence again. They both lifted their cups and looked at the empty house. "Are we getting started now, or what?"

"What do you think? The place is a mess inside? Did you notice the yard when we drove up?"

"We could hire somebody to clean it up," Tess said.

"We drove up today to start this today."

"That was before you insisted I pack this gin," Tess said. "Who could we call? Do you know anybody who lives here? I sure don't."

"We should have made the effort."

"Daddy's little girl," Tess said.

"That's not even funny, Tess. We're sitting in a dead man's drive."

"Thanks to you, I should say. This was your idea, Sis."

Karen thought, and then she said, "What if there's stuff in there that belonged to Mama?"

"After twenty years? She'll never miss it; she didn't take it with her. God knows she took everything else. Why should we care?"

"I just can't stand the thought of something of hers going in the trash without our knowing it."

"I rest my case. We wouldn't know it."

"We have to go in there now."

"Not before we finish this gin, we don't."

"Okay, then we have to get started."

But they didn't go inside, and it was after ten the next morning when they pulled into the drive that had been their father's. After they had finished the gin, Karen drove as best she could, following what hotel directions Tess could read. For an indeterminate time, they were lost in the small city where their father had lived alone for twenty years. In a synchronized moment, they looked up from a stoplight and saw their hotel beside them, like a wish come true.

"I think I believe in God," Karen said.

"I think you better shut up and drive," her younger sister said. "The light's green."

Their heavy breakfast—grits, eggs, and toast—had shored up their hangovers, but now the world was painted a mawkish gray. They didn't talk on the way to the house. Karen again parked at the top of the steep drive. When Tess opened her door, one of the Styrofoam cups tumbled onto the gravel drive. She watched as the wind lifted it and sent it head-over-heels down the scabby lawn toward the street. She remembered a childhood moment at the beach.

Karen was on the porch. "I hope you have the house key," she said.

Tess handed Karen her purse. "You look," she said. "I'm going around back and throw up."

"Do it here," Karen said. They were not completely sober.

Tess was already walking away. "Neighbors," she said.

"Never stopped Dad, I'd bet."

Karen left the door open. When Tess walked in, she saw her sister, hands on her hips, slowly rotating on her axis.

"I'll make a deal with you," Tess said.

"No. No way I'm cleaning up this mess by myself."

"We'll call someone with a giant vacuum to back up to the door and suck all this crap out of our lives."

"What's the deal you're offering?"

"I'll put a bullet through my brain."

"Tempting, but I'm not taking it. We'll start with the books. Stack them on the porch. We'll pile them in the van and take them to the library."

"Why didn't they go at the estate auction?"

"How would I know? Nobody reads anymore would be my guess. Make sure there's nothing in them before you put them outside."

"In the books? You mean money? Our old man? Not likely."

"Something of Mother's."

"In a book?"

"Some of them were *her* books. Just look, okay?"

Karen stood on a wobbly kitchen chair and handed the books down to her sister, then they both stacked them on the porch.

On the drive back from the library, Tess stopped for trash bags. Her sister was sitting on the floor of their father's study when Tess walked in. Karen didn't look up from the binder on her lap, didn't look up when she spoke. "I'd forgotten these. They were taken when we were babies." Tess looked over Karen's shoulder.

"Look at how young Mom was," Tess said. "She was a baby too."

They sat on the floor with the photo album between them. "There's another of these albums there, in the closet. How did they end up here? I wonder if Mom even knew he had them," Karen said.

"It's not the sort of thing you just forget, your history in pictures, I mean."

"I'm sure she must have had her reasons." Karen pointed. "That was your fourth birthday."

"Where are we?" Tess lifted up the album and tilted the picture for a closer look.

"Swan Lake," Karen said. "Look at those dresses—My Little Kitty, huh?" She pointed at a picture of the two of them petting a cat.

"Missy!" Tess said. "That was one surly, spiteful quadruped. I think she died of meanness."

Karen said, "Notice who's absent from all of these? No surprise, huh? He wasn't here even when he was here." She closed the album and looked at the clutter around them.

"We'll look through the other pictures at lunch, over a bucket of chicken. Fried chicken sounds good for a hangover. And beer. Definitely beer." Tess took a deep breath. "What's our plan of attack here?"

"Since you are the lawyer and I'm the minivan mom," Karen said, "I'll get rid of everything left in the kitchen and you can go through the filing cabinets. I wouldn't know what ought to be kept or for how long." They each took a roll of trash bags.

Tess filled the first bag with amber-colored warranties for long-discarded appliances: tools, mowers, tillers, TVs, stereo equipment and the like. Another trash bag overflowed with hundreds of newspaper and magazine articles and clippings on everything from ways to save electricity in 1980 to how to wash a dog.

Tess called to the kitchen: "Did Dad ever have a dog?"

"Hundreds of them," Karen shouted back.

"I mean the four-legged variety."

"Not that I know of."

Tess was tempted to skip the sorting, fill the bags, and get the trash to the street, pronto. But when she saw the file folders marked Taxes, Credit cards, Insurance, and Investments she acknowledged what she already knew: The dead couldn't clean up behind themselves. They could organize, but the sorting out belonged to somebody else.

When her older sister left to buy chicken and beer, Tess opened up a card table and two folding chairs in the kitchen. She thumbed through the photo albums as she waited.

"These were all taken at the beach, after he moved out," Tess said when Karen walked in.

"See this bag?" Karen said. Tess nodded. "It's not a very big bag, is it?"

"Big enough, I guess?" Tess said.

"But not huge, not massive, though; am I right?"

"Well, no."

"But what we see—or what we think you see—can be deceiving, wouldn't you say, Madame Prosecutor?"

"My professional experience bears that out."

Karen opened the bag, exposing its contents to Tess. "I'm stronger than I thought," she said. They were both smiling. "I never would have believed a bag of this size could hold ten thousand calories or that I would have enough muscle power to lift so much fat."

Tess would have to stop the automatic drafts for magazine subscriptions and the newspaper, pay off the final charges for utilities, turn in their father's cable equipment and cancel his phone. His car had been sold at the estate auction. He had neither asked nor informed Tess about assuming the responsibility of administering his estate. But when the registered letter arrived addressed to his executor, she'd not given it much thought. In fact, the call from Karen saying he was dead hardly registered higher on her scale of emotions than had the news been of a long-time client. His passing was another item on a list, one to be addressed when she got to it. Now she had gotten to it.

From the porch, the brown garbage bags at the bottom of the sloping lawn looked like a line of praying monks in the dwindling yellow light. Karen and Tess sat on the steps, knees apart, condensation from their beers beading on their fingers. Karen lifted her beer to the moon. "Next round's on you, Mom, for cleaning up his mess."

"Look at all that," Tess said, tilting her beer toward the brown trash bags.

"I would have left him, too," Karen said.

"I wonder what she would think, if she would feel anything. You know, she did marry him."

Karen looked down at the beer in her hand. "You stand there, you say the vows. I mean you *say* them, but you don't really know what you're saying. How can you?"

"It's always a risk. One I'm not willing to take, thank you very much," Tess said.

"Are you happy, single, I mean?"

"Are you happy, married, I mean?"

"I have my children."

"So did Mom, and she was so happy."

"She tried."

"Mama's little sword and shield."

"We have a lot to thank her for."

"Speak for yourself." Tess slowly stood, one hand holding the small of her back.

"I'm speaking for us both."

"Okay, big sister, you just go on speaking while I calculate the cost of back surgery."

"She was our mother. You should show a little respect."

"Why? You got Mom's great boobs. Not me."

"You got her brains, though."

"No, Sis. 'Fess up. Those came from Mr. Vacancy here."

"Where are you going?"

"I need food," Tess said. "Again." Then she trudged inside. Karen imagined her husband, Tom, and their two children now. Karen insisted on a routine, at the center of which was family. Re-creating what she had never had seemed like a plan for happiness. She glanced down at her watch. Tom was reading *Charlotte's Web* to Caroline, closing in on the final chapters. Mark had ten minutes more of his allowed PlayStation time.

Tess called. "Help!"

Karen saw that all the empty drawers in the kitchen had been pulled open.

"You don't think we threw away the phone book, do you? I'm ordering delivery."

The two sisters looked around as if they were in an empty gallery. Tess picked up the phone. "How do you call information?" she said.

"I'll get my cell," her sister said.

"Wait." Tess held her index finger to the facing of the kitchen door. "I'm calling this number."

"Dad's last girlfriend?" Karen said. "Think she delivers?"

"If Dad wrote her number on the wall, I'd guess so." Tess was dialing the number. She waited for someone to pick up. "Really?!" she said. Her eyes ballooned and turned to Karen. "You sure can help me. Yes. A large veggie pizza. Yes, that's the address." Tess hung up and turned to Karen. "Go figger," she said. "The pizza joint. We got time for a beer."

"What's this?" Tess said, exchanging money for the steaming pizza box. The kid handing her the small plastic cup was all pimples and brown teeth. At the bottom of the drive, the rear of his squat orange car wagged to the beat of the rap music that hammered its interior.

"Extra sauce," the kid said. "Mr. Killingsworth, he likes the extra sauce. He's always ordering from us. He's my regular customer. Most people, they snatch the box and slam the door in your face. Not him. Sometimes, he be standing here still talking when I drove away. Always a smile and a extra skin from Mr. Killingsworth. Mr. Killingsworth, he called me his friend."

"I hurt in places I didn't think I had," Tess said. "Do we have another trash bag?" She folded the top to the empty pizza box. "What's left?"

"I'm leaving most of his clothes on hangers for the Salvation Army," Karen said.

"We have to be out of here tomorrow by noon, Karen. I've got to administer some hardcore justice at ten on Monday. I have to be able to walk again by then."

The two sisters surveyed the remains of the kitchen. Karen said, "I guess we can leave the drapes and blinds up. Still, the bathrooms are a mess. Everything has five years of dust."

"I'm done. I'll call a cleaning service from the office. I'm done. We should have called someone from the start." The solitary overhead light cast grotesque yellow shadows. "None of Mom's pearls in this oyster, huh, Sis?"

"Peace of mind," Karen said. "Does that count?"

"Peace of mind?"

"Are all lawyers born cynics or does practicing law just make you that way?"

"I'm proud to say I come by it naturally."

"You can thank Dad for that."

"Thanks, Pop, wherever you are."

"We do have the pictures," Karen said. "You forgot the pictures. I'd call that a pearl. We found something we couldn't replace."

"Yes. Right." Tess pushed herself up slowly from the metal chair. "Time for a little walk—?"

"—What?"

"Down memory lane, Sis. Let's share a few obligatory saccharine moments before we fold this tent."

Karen pulled her chair so the two of them could look. Even after the beers Tess looked like a lawyer, the way she carried the albums tucked under her arm. She said, "Which ones haven't we seen?"

Karen opened one. "Ahhhh," she said. "These are all from the Debbie Boone summer at the beach."

Tess sang out of tune, "You liiite up my joint."

Karen pointed at a photo. "We've got some teenage angst happening in this one, don't we, Tess?"

The two studied the pictures. "Hey," Tess said. "Look at these. They are all the same picture." She pointed. "You. Mom in the middle. Me."

"She's looking right into the camera, isn't she?" Karen said. "Damn, that's a little spooky."

"She looks a little drunk in this one," Tess said.

"God, you're cynical. Just because she looks happy—"

"Look at me," Tess said. Karen turned. "Smile." Tess studied her face. "Yeah, Mom's a little loaded there. I can see it in your face. Besides, check out that hanging bathing suit strap. Mom's about to lose one. And she seems pretty happy about it."

"Tess—" Karen was laughing.

"Wait, wait," Tess said. She pulled the album in front of her and opened it to the last few pages.

"What are you doing?" Karen said. Her face was bright and full of smile.

Tess sighed. "I need another beer," she said. "I've discovered through careful photo analysis the source of my adult cynicism, its foundation, the before and after of that summer that has made me the woman—the unmarried woman, I might add—that I've become. Here lie the roots of my discontent."

Karen was laughing. "I'll get you that beer." When she sat down again, Tess held a page at the back of the book.

Tess said, "Look at this *before* picture. What do you see?"

"You. Mom in the middle with those smiling eyes looking through me. Me on the other side. What else? We're standing on the beach, the surf behind us?"

"Very good," Tess said. She was mocking the lawyer in her now. "Now Ms. Russell, look at this other photo, and tell me what you see."

"Same thing."

"Look closely, Ms. Russell. Closely. You must take into account what hangs, so to speak, in the balance here. How is this one different from the first one?"

Karen studied the two pictures. "Our tans are darker."

"Very good. This one was taken at the beginning of the summer, this one near the end."

"Mom is holding a glass in this one."

"Gin and tonic. That's a lime there, floating on top. What else?"

Karen looked at the picture, then up at her sister. "I don't know."

"You wouldn't."

"There is someone's shadow in this one," Karen said.

"You're still not looking," Tess said.

"I don't get it."

Tess pointed at Karen in the first picture, then at Karen in the second. "Boobs. You grew a whole cup size bigger in one summer. I hate you."

"I'd forgotten. The summer I turned eighteen. My summer of breasts."

"Summer of birth control pills." Tess pointed at the picture, at their mother's breasts, then at Karen's. "I look like a boy beside you two. I was a woman in a boy's body. I think I was a gay man. Now I'm a cynical lawyer."

"But you were only fifteen. Now you have breasts."

"Huh!" Tess said. "Compared to what?"

"But I've had babies. You wouldn't want to see them now."

"Liar! Look at Mom's. They're beautiful."

Karen whispered, "She's kinda letting them show, isn't she?"

"Perfect. You got the perfect breasts. Let's see yours. Take'm out, Sis."

The two were laughing now. Karen said, "I half expect her to speak to us from that picture."

"And what would she say?" Tess said.

"You liiite up my liiiife!" They were both laughing.

"Voice like that? No wonder we spent so much time on the beach, huh?" Tess said.

"And at the movies."

"And at the arcade."

"And at the pool."

"And at sleepovers."

"Weeee lit up our joints." The two sisters tilted up their beers. "I guess Mom needed a break from us, too," Karen said. "I mean after splitting with Dad that spring. Don't you think that's why she let us run free that summer, so that she could have time to clear her head?" She looked away from her sister. "I could use some mind time these days." Karen awaited Tess's reply.

Tess lifted the photo book. Her smile faded. "How did he get these? How did Dad get these pictures? Doesn't that strike you as odd?"

"Maybe after Mom died—"

"Who, other than you or me, would have even known about these?"

"Well, I'm glad we found them. Some memories here, huh, Tess?"

Tess studied the shots: herself, her mom, her sister. "These pictures, they all say the same thing." She brought her hand up to her mouth. Then: "They all say, 'We are here, and you are there. We are a family and you are not.'"

"Earth to Tess."

"No. Look. That's what they say."

"That's not what I see," Karen said, drumming the side of her beer bottle with her nails.

"She sent these to him; that's how he got them. She sent them."

"Why would she do that? You don't know what you're saying."

"She sent them, Karen."

"She wasn't like that. Besides, even if she did, even if what you say is true, we *were* a family, you, Mom and me. We were. Always. Look." Karen reached for the other album. "See? Even when we were babies? Look at them, Tess. You, me, and Mom. We were always the family."

"Who took those, Karen?"

"What are you getting at?"

"He took them. Why didn't Mom take pictures of you and me and Dad?"

"I don't like what you're saying?"

"I'm saying that he's not in any of these because he was taking the pictures. What I'm saying is that maybe we're looking at an act of love here."

"I can't believe you're defending him."

"All I'm saying is that there was someone behind the camera, okay, someone who was seeing each moment that these pictures represent, that he is the reason we see what we see here. He was a participant in every one of these."

Karen drained the last of her beer, held the bottle up high. "Thanks, Dad, you shit."

"Gee, Karen, I didn't mean to—"

"It was you and me and Mom. Remember. That's where it starts, that's where it ends. She was the one who took us shopping and came to our soccer games and made us up for the prom and dried our tears when our young hearts were broken. And where was he?"

"At work."

"He moved out."

"Uhmm. Let's list his choices."

"He was a jerk."

"Yep. The man was a jerk. No argument there."

"You make your living winning arguments, Tess."

"I withdraw the question."

At the hotel, they showered and then watched TV in silence.

"You still have that?" Karen nodded toward Tess's open suitcase. Tess lifted her nightgown from it.

"Yes," Tess said. She pointed at her mother's raised initials in the leather. "It was my gift from their divorce."

In bed, Tess closed her eyes.

She woke. The room was dark. The dim light of Karen's cell phone cast dark shadows over her eyes. "Just because, Tom," she whispered. "Just *because*, I said."

After locking the door to the house that had been their father's, Tess offered to drive. Karen handed her the minivan keys. Karen slept. Tess stopped in Augusta to fill up. Karen took the keys. Tess slept. When she woke, the afternoon clouds over Atlanta looked like a red and purple tide retreating into darkness. Karen parked outside Tess's garage and hit the button to unlock their doors.

"Want a cup of coffee, Sis?" Tess set down the small suitcase that had been their mother's. Inside it were their father's remains: folders containing his assets, his liabilities.

Karen looked at her watch. She had returned to full-gauge minivan mom. "Can't do it," she said. "Call me."

"Okay, I'll do that."

Karen shifted into reverse. Tess had lifted the suitcase and stepped into the bright lights of the van when the click, click of the shifting transmission stopped her. She looked back. Karen's window was coming down. Tess looked into the bright lights. "Wait," Karen said from the darkness.

She turned and reached into the back seat. "Take these."

"You don't want them?"

"No."

"When you're over, we can go through them again, maybe find some nice frames."

"I don't want them," Karen said.

Tess started a hot bath, then poured herself a glass of red wine. She was already into Monday, into the mind that she would take to court. She undressed and tested the water. She thought she might review the cases and soak her tired bones. Walking naked from the bathroom to her study for the briefs, she reflected upon the small pleasure of nakedness. No husband or children to shield or hide from.

Easing into the steaming bath, she closed her eyes. A levitating moment followed. She felt her limbs rise, her breasts surrender. Then she was seeing the snapshots from that summer. Her sister, their mom, herself.

There's someone's shadow in this one.

Tess couldn't remember his name. Mr. Finch? Dove? It was a bird's name. The man with the mustache. The man with the camera hiding most of his face. The man three houses down the beach. Darling? Starling. Mr. Starling. "Say hello to Mr. Starling, Tess," her mother said. "He's one of my bridge friends. He's going to take our picture."

Mr. Starling had been a professional singer and actor. That's all Tess could remember, and that Mr. Starling seemed always to be on the beach when she and Karen and their mother were there. Never on the beach when only she and Karen were there. That their mother had spent a lot of time with her "bridge friends" that summer. That Mr. Starling had given Karen and her tickets to see *Dirty Dancing*, claiming he'd won them from the radio station. That Karen cried out, "103X!?" That Mr. Starling didn't know the station's call numbers. That when she and Karen ran into Mr. Starling, he never took his eyes from Karen when he spoke to the two of them. That once she had said to Karen, "Do you think his name is really Starling. I mean, isn't that like so fake sounding?"

"He's gorgeous," Karen had said, twittering about. "What other name *could* he have?"

There's someone's shadow in this one.

A clairvoyant memory. Tess sat up in the bath. Where was Karen? she thought. She could not remember. Tess had been alone on the beach sunbathing. Her mother was playing bridge. Where was Karen? She remembered now that it was their last week at the beach, that she had been reading a crime novel, that she was determined to finish it before they packed up to leave and that her skin, even after almost three months of tan, was tender, that she had challenged the late summer sun. She dropped the book inside her beach bag and folded her towel. Above the horizon, a slate line of clouds promised evening rain.

After washing the sand from her feet and legs outside, Tess entered the house barefoot and padded down the carpeted hall. The quiet house felt empty. Then she glimpsed a reflection in the full-length mirror that hung from her mother's bedroom closet door.

Her mother stood naked, arms loosely at her side, the white skin of her breasts and hips in sharp relief against her dark brown flesh. Tess wanted to turn back, but she felt trapped between embarrassment and fascination. Movement seemed impossible. She watched as her mother's hands slowly traced her hips, her fingers floating at her stomach, and finally cupping her breasts. Then her shoulders folded like a bird's wings, and when her hands went up to cover her eyes, Tess tiptoed past. She had seen her mother cry, of course. But she'd never seen her naked mother cry. At the end of the hall, she closed her bedroom door, lay on her bed, plugged in her Walkman headphones, cranked the volume, and blasted that picture away. She was only fifteen.

Tess stepped from the bath, turned to the mirror, and watched as she gently dried with the soft white towel. And she thought of her mother, naked, crying: two teenage daughters, eighteen and fifteen, a broken marriage, a summer lover she would never see again, maybe her last lover. Like herself, middle-aged. Tess studied her own nakedness.

She decided to leave the bathroom door ajar, thinking its pale nightlight might be what she needed. Tess set the clock. She again closed her eyes and thought of her mother and Karen. Her father behind this camera, Mr. Starling behind that one. She considered motive and opportunity. She pictured her father. Motive and opportunity. Her mother. Karen. Motive and opportunity. She reflected upon the years that had stretched from there to here, the ones that would stretch from here to there. She tried to find the right word. Not forgiveness. Something else.

And soon she slept—slept comfortably in that place of darkness and no time, without dreaming even, and in the morning woke a minute before the alarm could shatter that serene place that was no place. Then, rising slowly, feeling the aches of her father's house, she followed the smell of coffee into her kitchen, allowing her gown to hang open, her nakedness to show for no one to see, and poured a first cup, then sat in the semidarkness, sipped with eyes closed, and listened to the silence. She pictured the contents of the suitcase which rested beside a chair in her study, her father's papers, two fading collections of snapshots. She drank her coffee without haste.

Tess stood slowly, feeling the tightness in her muscles, the promise of pain in her limbs. She walked barefoot down the quiet hall, looking neither this way nor that, toward the suitcase. She would begin the process of sorting and filing her father's life.

The dim light of the kitchen was behind her. And with each step, she entered the edge of her own shadow, which floated before her in the silent hall. A word formed at her lips, and as her mother's suitcase came into view she spoke:

"Generosity," she whispered. "Generosity."

Diane Szabo/O Mysterious Night

Cold air, bare trees.
There is more to this story
than the bones of winter.

Cycle after cycle, clue upon clue
we try to live
with the silence of the woods,
glad for every bird
which didn't fly south.

Night comes, and the moon,
a half-clad blond, reveals
deer tracks in the snow.

Is this, then, how Death comes:
stripped, silent, white;
lulling us the way the wind
sings the winter world to sleep?

Is it enough to say,
all things sleep to rise again,
when all we have is a promise
and the few tracks we've left behind?

Tracy DeBrincat/Questionnaire

What did it feel like when you fell into the water.
Were you glad to be gone from your life full of trouble—
your hysterical girlfriend, guilty and pregnant,
not even certain she'd ever had sex, still hazy on the subject of reefer.
Did you wish her clothes had been all the way off.
Or did you prefer half-undressed: white breast pushing out of crooked
    cup,
shirt peeled away from one shoulder.
Did you think you were just going to kiss her goodnight.
Had you meant to pull out. Had you promised.
Was it better when you came inside. Were you instantly sorry.

Or once you both knew it was already too late, did you
do it like dogs in summer, growling and tearing.
Did you suddenly find reasons to explore moonlit side streets.
Frequent libraries. Take taxis to nowhere roundtrip.
Did she ever come back from the ladies' room and hand you her panties.
Was that before or after she missed her period.
Do you remember when she told you on that dogs of summer
couch, and there was *just no way*.
Do you remember fighting. With her. With your family.
Why didn't you tell them all to fuck off.
Or did she not want to get married either.

Did you speak to her the day you went sailing. Remember to kiss her
    goodbye.
Was it a tragic, arms-around-the-neck, movie sort of kiss, the
kind that seals the fate of bright, young lives. Or was
it the quick peck, the one that takes destiny for granted.
Was it exciting to sail into the swell. Did you think about sharks.
Did you think about her. Did you dive down smiling.
Look back up to the surface. Hear someone faintly calling your name.
Was it liberating to empty your heart and fill your lungs.
Did you look forward to it. Hope it might happen sooner.
Didn't it?

Jack Ridl/Searching Again for My Father

I have looked through the garage, shelves
stacked with engine oil, cans of paint, piles
of rags and gloves and old hats, boxes
of shoes, nails, broken saw blades, clocks.

And in the crab apple tree he planted
in the back left corner of the yard,
in its burst of white blossoms, in
the empty sparrow nest that has sat
between the fork in a branch for years.

Maybe here, I think, across the room,
sleeping in front of the summer-empty
fireplace, or sitting on the mantel looking
toward the closed white kitchen door.

Or here, right here, in this chair, scribbling
across this very notebook, smiling at each
fallen word, thinking *I still don't know why.*

In the basement? Opening the Army steamer
trunk, taking out the medals, the Captain's
bars, the box of letters, and the pen and ink
drawings he found within the rubble of France.

Or under the dining table, where the dog
sleeps, breathing softly, velvet eyelids ready
to rise at the sound of "Walk," ragged toy lion
lying drool-enameled by his dream-twitching nose.

Or maybe in the sigh at the day's end. Maybe
in the last twenty pages of the book I've been
reading for a week. Maybe I passed by him
at the opening of Chapter Four, when I wondered
why the writer, without warning, shifted point of view.

Joanne Lowery/Lou Reed at the Pumpkin Patch

In the fake barn among fake cobwebs
the boombox wails of sex and luck,
a voice singed by repeated trips to hell,
drugs and death on city streets,
friends lost to the wild side.

The pumpkins bussed in from Georgia
are veined and turgid and stalked.
But even the ugly ones feel round
with pleasure, skin encasing mush
and seeds strung together for the future.

Darling, pick me. I am more solid
than I look, something you'll need
two hands to carry. Carve me
a face to flicker secrets:
vines, music and hips,
the trick or treat of love,
nights of black velvet.

Joanne Lowery/Hysteria

Like a mouse it flew through the window
and undid my hair.
I cannot bear this life.
The lanks that hung over my ears
to hush some woman's weeping
rose up and unfurled into wings.
I followed over rooftops,
my breast beating against the wind.
All this came from a womb
three-pointed as a bird beak.
Part of me wished the doctor
could see how down below
everyone is a woman.

Marjorie Power/The Glove

The little glove, its mitten clip.
The glove under the table.
Under the kitchen sink.
The rubber glove, sweaty inside.

The ivory kid glove tooled with flowers.
That remembers the wedding.
That wants to be a boot.
That kept its mate.

The two stored in tissue.
The brown glove, drying.
Its leather gone stiff.
The other glove.

Her oven mitt.
His surgical glove.
The cat burglar's hush.
The glove in the waste bin.

The white lace, child sized, torn thumb glove.
The glove that made the tabloids.
The glove in the sale bin.
In the dumpster.

In the unlocked locker.
At the back of the garage.
That old baseball mitt.
The glove grown too small.

The glove still used for touchy subjects.
The fat expensive ski glove.
The ambidextrous mitten.
The parrot-like colors.

The Andes, their fingered flutes.
The gold bracelet, the glove elbow length.
The glove, the tango, the crescent, the thigh.
The new mitten

lost outside the library.
The boxing glove, the televised fight.
The artist's model, her hand.
The glove he paints there.

Marjorie Power/Second Reading

Here's a detail I hadn't absorbed:
a wooden table painted green.

Another just like it
appears in chapter five
after the action moves
from farm to city.
Gambling, lust, laughter. . . .
And towards the end of the book,
a green table. Another country now.
A different time.

The last table mentioned
is all that's left
in a cottage, after a war.
The cottage dwellers were a couple
in love. One remains alive.
High summer. Scent of hay.
Asters. Daisies. Queen Anne's Lace.

❖❖❖

The departed still come
to table, in their own way.
They appreciate a vase of wildflowers.
They want us to enjoy our meals
and one another's company.
They like us to speak of them
but only once in awhile.
And not in sorrow.

As for my lifelong friend
who fell out of touch
for the past year and a half:
she has fallen in with disappointment

and unwittingly married it.
A little time lost between us
used to make no difference.
Now I wouldn't know
where to seat her, what
to serve or discuss.

Talena Smith/Her Inhuman Life

an illusion; i'm eminently an illusion,
they don't call me fake for nothing,
time slows—my soul is sold in five,
four, three, two,
one.

this isn't earth,
but i don't travel space—
i stand at the edge of everyone's vision,
waiting to jump; on three,
two,
one.

and this isn't death,
yet i don't know life—
just a phantom, always a phantom,
unaware of what they support,
cheer me on, louder,
louder.

but it's quiet now, the show over—
i'm alone, always alone,
two of them left,
now one, one—
me.

the last thing i said was,
"dying will be the most human thing i've done."

and i was right.
always right.

George Looney/Driving at Night in a Storm

Rain. Roads awash
in colors,
hesitant. Each pair

of headlights touches
their ghosts
in acceleration. Rain

takes up the cause of
reflection, surfaces
trying to manifest enough

dappled echoes of light
to be reminiscent,
in the dark, of daylight

when the accidental blurs
of house sparrows
turn the sky, forgiven,

into the inevitable sprawl
of occurrence
and desire we say it is,

given the chance. Tonight,
rain's an elixir.
A child's chalk hopscotch

grid has almost
been erased
by this scrubbing.

So much washed clean
tonight. Pray
some sin remains.

Jennifer Campbell/Below

Ducks coast effortlessly,
oarlike legs invisibly slicing the depths.
So much happens below the surface.
You went after the cat one day
with a wooden stick, marking
your territory with every thump.
In horror movies, in an always-fall setting,
characters discover sex and death at once.
Blazing oranges make a rich palette
of fear. Children's sharp laughter
chopped by the breeze.
It's more common to get clocked
in the head by a falling apple
than you might think.

Laura Madeline Wiseman/Hypotheses
(or In the Lake of the Woods)

They were unhappy. The lake droned. She clutched
the sack of her belly. He unplugged the phone.

They sunbathed, spread blankets on the porch
and tried to touch like younger versions of themselves.

Their marriage flickered with her clandestine kisses
and his Vietnam. The night passed. They slept (hypothesis).

What he recalls: crouching by the bed and tipping the kettle
over the plants, a tropical stink, and the hum of flies.

What he found in the morning: her absence, a Minnesota
in a foot of snow, a boat gone, and vodka bottles.

There is evidence. There are guesses. For John Wade
all there is, is this: humping and a VC with a hoe.

Kevin Griffith/The Only Good Writer is a Dead One

There are more poems in the world
Than empty beer bottles.
—Lindley Williams Hubbell

I remember my first assignment well. A sloppy job in retrospect. Very careless. My target was a male, 45, who had received an M.F.A. seventeen years ago, but was still hanging around university coffee houses, hogging up all the time during open mic nights. The best he could do for a "living" was occasional adjunct jobs at the local community college, or, if he was real lucky, a freshman comp course at the same university where he had been a grad student. Truly pathetic. What's worse, he had started his own small press and used the promise of a possible chapbook publication as a way to lure naïve coeds who were "into" poetry.

I attended a weekly poetry reading at one of the bars near the university and arrived just as he was taking the mic. Let me tell you, there is no more horrifying sight than a middle-aged man trying to look hip by wearing ripped jeans and a Ramones T-shirt. Once he started reading, things only got worse. For his first poem, he tried performing a hip-hop version of the Prologue to the *Canterbury Tales*. When he was finished, only one person was clapping, and I think it was because the 7:00 dollar-a-bottle beer special had just kicked in.

Then, his face suddenly grew serious, and he uttered those words that still, even years later, strike loathing into the heart of poetry audiences everywhere: "I wrote this poem the day after 9/11."

The poem started out fine, but then descended into a chant in which he shouted "Burning/Flaming. . . Flaming/Burning" slowly and, ugh, *with feeling*, for about forty seconds, until I just couldn't take it anymore. Ignoring all my training, I simply stood up, pulled my Glock .45 ACP with silencer from under my hand-woven, all-natural dyed Peruvian wool turtleneck, and planted a slug right in the center of his forehead.

No one in the bar moved. No one dived under a table or rushed me in an effort to take away my gun. In fact, as I turned to hurry out of the place, there was a smattering of applause, and, as I approached the exit, someone pulled me aside and offered to buy me a drink.

❖❖❖

I live alone in a small apartment on the east side of the city. Assassins are by nature lonely. I did have a girlfriend, though. Once. The problem is that writers tend to gravitate toward other writers. Her name was Melia. Jet-black hair and a nice full set of lips. We had been dating for three months, when one morning she woke up and just announced out of the blue, "I want to write a memoir."

"A memoir? But you're only twenty-three years old."

"Yes, but my story should be told. No, *must* be told."

"But, uh, what would you write about?"

"There is so much about me that you don't know, babe." She pursed her lips and put one hand on her hip. I always loved that move. It hurts to remember it now. "Like, did you know that my parents actually put me in public school for three weeks in the fourth grade? It was horrible. I'm still scarred by it. And don't forget that I worked for almost a month as a literacy volunteer at that church downtown. I saw the worst of the worst. But I completely transformed their lives, just like that teacher in that education movie, you know, the 'Whatever of Whatever' or something like that."

I really liked Melia, but not enough, I guess, to break my vow of secrecy and warn her about the very real danger that lay ahead for her if she pursued this madness.

I hoped that it was just a phase, but it only got worse. She was not discreet at all. She openly referred to herself as a "memoirist" and started a small writing group that, as its first project, had to read and critique her manuscript.

I came back to our apartment one day, and she was just gone. There were some slight signs of a struggle—a pillow on the floor, a chair tipped over—but not much. I knew it was the agency's work. I received an e-mail a few weeks later informing me that her headless body had been found floating off the coast of Turkey.

On Mondays, I meet with my "mentor" from the agency, Mike. Mike is a senior agent who has been assigned to keep watch over me, teach me the finer points of killing, offer his wisdom, and all that other bullshit mentors do.

We are at the shooting range today, engaging in a little target practice. The targets aren't the usual red bull's eye diagrams you would normally imagine. No, today we are practicing on photos and sketches of forgotten minor American poets of the early twentieth century. I set my sight on Thomas Hornsby Ferril and score three hits on his face.

"Look, I just shot Rolfe Humphries right in the ascot." Mike lifts the tip of his revolver's barrel to his lips and blows on it. "Sweet." In the parlance of boy's pant sizes, Mike would definitely be referred to as "husky," though he is surprising graceful and light on his feet when he needs to be. His hair is black and coifed into a swirl that looks like Big Boy's, and he gives off an aroma that's a combination of Old Spice and Hai Karate. Mixing "retro" scents was really big in men's grooming trends a few years back. But it's not anymore. Mike's always a little behind the curve.

"You and writers just don't mix, Mike." I watch as the face of Babette Deutsch slides into range. God, she was homely.

"Dude, it's not that I hate all writers. I'm a discerning hater. I mean, take a guy like Lord Byron. Now that guy had balls. Had spine. He fell on the thorns of life and bled, man. Nowadays, everyone wants the glory without the damn thorns. No sense of having to earn anything." He leans over and shoots Babette for me. Her face is now just a big black hole.

"I mean, you don't see the face of Shakespeare, Gertrude Stein, or even Vonnegut popping up here, right?"

"But don't you ever wonder if it is all worth it. Doing what we're doing? You kill one mediocre writer and three more appear to take her place. Shouldn't we just let the test of time do its work? Look at these poor saps we're using as target practice. No one reads them anymore."

"We *are* the test of time now, man. Don't you get it? You can't rely on the old paradigm anymore. Did I just say 'paradigm'? Fuck. If I say something that pretentious again, I want you to shoot *me*, okay?"

I laugh and pop a few rounds into the space where Babette's face used to be. "I guess you're right. But how do we know we're not taking someone out who might be the next Vonnegut?"

"Are you slipping, man?" Mike looks at me in a way I haven't seen him look at me before. Very seriously. Very out-of-character. It's almost a little chilling. He furrows his brow and his eyes give a stare that could cut through ice. I can see why he is my superior. "Listen," he continues, rubbing his weapon with a silk handkerchief, "in my book, we aren't killing nearly enough writers. For one thing, the agency won't authorize the killing of those fucks who win a Pulitzer or National Book Award early in their careers and then just pump out parodies of themselves for the next twenty years. The agency says that, in spite of their relentless mediocrity, they'd be missed. That's not what I think, baby. I think we would be doing the world an even bigger favor. But I don't make the rules."

I nod my head. All the fun has gone out of our meeting. Mike hands his ear-protectors to an assistant.

"Take care of yourself," he says. "Remember the mission. You're the test of time, baby, and don't forget it."

❖❖❖

When I get back to my apartment, Mary is still there, tidying up the place. Mary is a single mom who dropped out of college as a sophomore and now makes a living by piecing together various jobs. Housekeeping is one of them. I really don't need my apartment to be cleaned—hell, it's just a one-bedroom decked out with a few pieces of cheap black-leather furniture and almost nothing to dust in it—but she needs the cash and is a very sweet woman. She comes by once a week to straighten things up with her own brand of "organic and all-natural" house cleaning products.

"I tried a new toilet cleaner today I made with lemon juice, baking soda, and essence of lavender." Mary is holding a toilet brush in her hand and seems really proud of her accomplishment.

"That's great. I can really smell the difference." For once, I am not being sarcastic. I really *can* smell the difference. "So how is Toby doing?"

"He's with his grandma now, probably watching the computer and eating way too much candy." Toby is her five-year-old son. She laughs and uses her free hand to adjust her ponytail ever so slightly. She's about my age, 30, and has a very honest beauty to her. A few freckles on her cheeks, blue eyes, and everything in its place. Nothing to knock you out with, but nothing to complain about either.

"Well, so here you go." I hand her five twenties. That's more than what she charges, but what am I going to spend it on anyway? Another book of poetry?

"Hey, I hear you write stuff." She looks awkwardly at her feet. "Poetry, I mean."

Oh God, I think. "Yes, that's true. Had some things published. How did you find out?"

"Well, you know, I may just be a lowly maid, but I read. Even those hoity-toity lit journals sometimes."

"Sorry, didn't mean to put down your reading habits. Well, I'm glad you noticed my work." Actually I'm not. Really really not.

"I write poetry." She looks up to my eyes.

Here it comes, I think.

"Could you look at some of my work sometime? I mean, I want someone who knows something to read it and give me a really honest opinion."

There's no way out. "Okay, bring some next time. Be glad to do it."

Mary smiles and picks up her supplies. "See ya next week," she says at the door. "With some poetry."

Lucky me.

❖❖❖

My next assignment is a pleasure. I have to take out a thirty-nine-year-old creative writing prof at a small private college near the city. His file is a hoot. He has, over his "career," published almost two-hundred short stories, but mostly in journals with names like *Boink*, *Lutheran Thoughts*, and *The Best Fiction in the Universe, 2019*. His publicity photo is included with his file. He is actually wearing a tweed jacket and leaning against a bookshelf that contains what looks like only his work and Hemingway's.

When I arrive at his office, he is eager to let me in. I am posing as an editor for a big textbook publisher who is interested in his proposal for yet another creative writing textbook. That's when you know you've hit rock bottom as a writer—when you start writing textbooks that purport to teach others your own special brand of mediocrity.

"So, tell me about your idea for this book. Uh, what's it called again?" I pretend to take notes on my computer writing pad.

"It's called *Fiction for the Clueless*." He leans over his desk and weaves his fingers together. "I wanted to use 'clueless' in the title, to keep it very hip, you know."

"I see. So what makes it unique? I mean, how does it separate itself from the other three thousand books on writing that are published each year?"

"Well, it will be the first textbook that is word free. Only visuals. A picture book, actually. And it will use up to seven different colors."

"So it's a book on writing that has no writing in it?" Killing this guy is going to be so much fun.

"Yeah, you know how students are these days. They all want to write, but none of them wants to read anything. Why fight it? They're all 'visual learners,' you know." He hands me a sample page he himself has sketched.

It shows a "writer" sitting at a desk, rubbing his hand over his chin. "This is part of the chapter called 'Getting Started,'" he says.

I point to the office window. "That's a very beautiful tree there. What kind is it?"

As he gets up and walks to the window, all the while lecturing me on the virtues of magnolias, I quickly pour a vial of cyanide into his coffee mug, which is almost full of steaming coffee. I have decided that a bullet would be too painless for this one.

I stand up, interrupting his tree monologue. "Well, let me just say that I think your idea is brilliant. At least 100k in royalties the first year. This calls for a toast." I hold up my travel mug to my lips and he does the same with his mug.

"Cheers!"

I can already hear his students shouting with joy after they find out their class has been cancelled.

I am back in my apartment, reading the newspaper, when my eyes lock on to an article. It's buried in the "Life" section. Two small columns under the title "Writers in the News." First, it seems that the former poet laureate of the United States, a guy who had published thirty-six books over the last thirty-five years, was seriously injured when he was run over by a Humvee. The funny thing was that no one saw anyone driving the Humvee. I remember now that the agency tried out remote-controlled assassination vehicles a few years back, but gave up because they were simply too inefficient. Case in point with the poet laureate. "Seriously injured" just doesn't cut it in the assassination game. In other news, a famous female novelist, who has somehow lived to be 123 years old after rising to prominence in the late eighties and early nineties, was apparently hit by a blowgun dart as she gave a reading at Princeton. The dart had no effect, though, probably because her circulation was too slow to deliver the poison to a vital part of her body. I remember what Mike told me at the shooting range. About how the agency should extend its range of targets to include bigger fish. But the agency itself would never do that. It would call too much attention to itself, get the F.B.I.'s interest, among other things. We'd be covert no more. I am beginning to wonder if Mike's gone rogue.

On Wednesday, my cellphone buzzes. I answer and it's Mike. He's canceling our appointment for this Monday. I can hear semis idling in the background. It sounds like he is calling from a truck stop. He tells me that he's decided to go rogue.

❖❖❖

Well, now I am caught between the proverbial rock and a hard place. Or should I say solid lead bookend and a hard place. No, I shouldn't. Too lame. But whatever the strained metaphors, I have to contemplate my next move. The agency is very tricky. Maybe Mike really hasn't gone rogue, but is testing me, seeing if I have the guts to report him to Internal Affairs. But if I do that, and he's not fooling, he will certainly hunt me down and kill me. If I do nothing, and the agency finds out that I know he's rogue, agents will hunt us both down and kill us. Maybe Mike is hoping that I'll take his lead and try popping off a few National Book Critics Circle Award winners or a MacArthur genius. But that's way too risky, and, hell, some of those writers are indeed very talented. People have to read something of quality, right?

I decide on the "do-nothing" option. It's always the easiest.

❖❖❖

Mary comes on Monday, for the usual housekeeping, and she is eager to show me a few pages of poetry.

"Like I said, be honest." She brushes a few strands of hair away from her face and sticks her hands deep into her jeans' pockets. I think she really does want me to be honest. Usually, when people say that, they want to hear what they want to hear, not the truth. Maybe if more people told the truth, I wouldn't be in the mess I'm in now.

I look at the pages she's handed me. And I'll be goddamned, but they look like they have been typed on an actual old-fashioned typewriter. IBM electric. And the poems, well, I can't believe it, but they are simple and clear. No tricks. She has written one about hearing Toby's first words and it's completely unsentimental and filled with imagery I haven't encountered before.

"Wow, I can't believe it, but these are really good." I smile at her.

"You can't believe it?" She crosses her arms over her chest.

"Oh, I'm sorry. I didn't mean that I didn't think you were capable. . . well, you know what I mean. It's just that it's been so long since I have read anything so sincere. And you typed them on a typewriter?"

"My grandmother's. Mom saved it when Grandma died. I just like the feel of the keys. Plus, it keeps me from saying too much."

We sit on the couch together. She leans close to me, and I can feel the warmth of her body. It's not something I've felt for a long time.

"This one, about Toby, it's particularly good. You know just how to end a poem. I loved it." Her work reminds me of Yehuda Amichai's, the poet whose work inspired me to write. Years back.

"I'm really, really glad. And you know what?" She rests her hand on my knee.

"What?"

"I've been asked to read at Joe's Books. They have an open mic on Wednesdays. I'll be the featured reader. I would really like you to come. It will help with my nervousness."

Oh boy. I haven't attended a poetry reading, at least without the intent to kill, in years.

"Sure. I'll be there."

She moves even closer, and for a moment seems like she's going to kiss me, but then she suddenly stands up straight. "Well, I better get to the cleaning. Lots to do, huh?"

❖❖❖

I'm reading "Writers in the News" again. A former National Book Award winner and author of eleven novels, none better than her first, has died. She fell into the sting ray tank at the Riverhead Aquarium on Long Island and was barbed to death. A few witnesses say she was pushed, but there is no concrete evidence of foul play. I know for a fact that Mike hated her work. I have to give him points for creativity.

❖❖❖

My next assignment comes through, just as it should. No signs that the agency is aware of Mike's going AWOL or my knowledge of it. My target is an overweight, 55-year-old "spoken word" poet. He is being interviewed by the local low-power public radio station tomorrow. I am supposed to wait for him outside the station, leap out of the bushes, and strangle him with piano wire. Why is the agency making me waste my time with this loser? No publications. Purely local. I decide to take a pass. Our contract allows us to take one mental health day every six months.

Quite honestly, Mary's poetry has been making me rethink my whole mission in life. I used to believe, strongly believe, that the agency had a clear and noble purpose, and I was part of some effort greater than myself to preserve culture for future generations. But then, someone like Mary comes along. Who are we to decide what writer lives and dies? I mean, what if we accidentally kill the next big one? The next Shakespeare? During my training, my superiors assured me that all potential targets were carefully screened to make sure we were eliminating just the buffoons and no talents. But, as the saying goes, there's no accounting for taste. And what if the agency's tastes aren't the right ones?

During my ruminations, I've been cleaning my gun. I place it back in its case and then lock it in my solid walnut gun cabinet. I look at the key in my hand. I walk to the window, open the screen and then throw it into the night air, counting the seconds it takes to fall ten stories before it makes a ping, and, hopefully, bounces into an open sewer grate.

My cell buzzes. Probably Mike, wondering why I haven't told the agency what I know, or why I haven't gone rogue myself. But it's Mary. She just wants to talk. About writing. About why words matter. It's a good talk.

❖❖❖

I'm at Mary's poetry reading. Joe's Books, is, as they say, a quaint place, smelling of old paperbacks and popcorn that the owner, an elderly guy who gave up trying to make money years ago, still gives out for free to anyone browsing the shelves. There are about eight other people here, people I've never met before, but who must be friends of Mary's or diehards who always come to these things.

Mary is reading at the front, each word slipping from her lips in a way that makes her poems seem even better. As she finishes, the crowd claps politely and a little bell rings as a new customer comes in the front door.

I don't even turn to look at who it is. All I have to do is smell the unmistakable fragrance of Old Spice Karate to know that it's Mike. He plops down in the empty seat next to mine and munches on some popcorn he is shoveling out of the bag.

"This popcorn rocks," he says. "The best. Made with palm oil."

"I read about the writer in the sting ray tank, Mike."

"That was pretty clever, wasn't it? But today, I've got nothing fancy. Just a good, old-fashioned hit." He pats his chest, where his gun is holstered under his black polyester sports coat.

I shift my eyes to Mary, who is now introducing her fourth poem. "Mike, not her," I whisper.

"The fuck you talking about?" A piece of popcorn falls from Mike's mouth. "Her? No way, baby. I came here for you. I can't take any chances you'll rat me out."

Thank God. "Then let's go," I say. I don't want Mary to see the mess that's about to happen here.

"What's your hurry? Sit and enjoy the rest of the reading." He leans back into his folding chair, tipping it onto the two back legs. "By the way, that chick up there is good, damn good. Makes me wish I could write something I cared about again."

"Me too." I let go of a breath I've been holding way too long. "Me too."

Carine Topal/What I Would Have Done

I would have sat my father down.
I would have pulled up a chair
and face-to-faced him.

I would have growled back
and finally not taken his shit.
I would have brought up my mother

just to watch him cry,
something to keep him in the present.
You think I'm stupid, he'd say.

I'd bring up my dead brothers and the son-
in-law he called *a horse's ass.*
He would have listened like a monk.

And like a monk, cross-legged on a throne,
he'd show me nothing of what he was
thinking. I would have felt twelve again,

between worlds of abstinence
and hunger, while he was imagining
the Bird Lady and the Monkey Man.

I would have forced him to walk
through the flooded rooms
of the second floor and explain

the water still running in his sink.
Why the front door's been open
since last Tuesday and why we plan

to take his keys if he tries to step inside
his car. Knowing what I know, I still
would have moved him into that home,

left him, pacemaker and all, with the
talkative matron, his hearing aid dismantled.
And he still would have died in the hallway,

a month later, on the red floral carpet.
But I would have fed his lungs
with my breath, I would have talked him

into staying long enough to hear his bitter
call, a plea to save him, and hand him his
glasses, so he could finally see.

Cully Pappas/Deception

The traitor comes disguised as loving friend.
He hides his treachery in kindly words
And, smiling, soothes the fears outsiders send
To timid souls whose dreams are often blurred.
A Judas walks along the sacred path,
So sweetly spewing promises untrue
That, once uncovered, cannot hide the wrath
With which his rotted soul is thus imbued.
How stealthily the promise creeps along,
Surprising all who truly thus believe
Such solemn oaths surpass religious song—
Above the clouds, they soar in Godly eaves.
Be not deceived by serpent's artful tongue
Nor blind to promises on falsehoods hung.

Mark Taksa/The Awakening

The student looks up at my hand lifting the book.
As if it is a blouse with tight sleeves,
she struggles to live in the narrative—
of the herder who breathes the scent of a wolf—

my voice carries like wind over the field.
The scent bleeds from her hair.
Her voice I have never heard
asks a question that could be a growl.

For the child of a father who talks about twisting bolts
past the hour his wrists lose strength,
so his daughter has cake for her birthday,
and then his fist pounds down on her,

and then opens to scoop food
from her plate, any answer can be a growl.
The angle of the girl's glance shows wolf bones.
The wolf must escape her dress.

Mark Taksa/Magical Wrench

My car is a Buddha sleeping with my key
in his belly. I cannot coax a yawn
out of the engine. I am late to the airport.
The woman I love will be alone
on a couch on a beach under a sun that melts
all moods into romance. She will have surplus love
and make room for a competitor.

My tools are in my neighbor's house
quiet as a hall after a concert. He is a violinist
who saw music in the manual for auto repair.
He was fired for wrong wrenching.

At the roses between our houses,
he told me about looking for magic
when he feels contrariness in his muscles.
I gave him my tools and told him I believed
in magic, though I could not define it.

I suggested he practice on my car
until he knew the magic of right wrenching.
Lately, I have been waiting by the roses,
but the song of his strings has been as hushed.

I knock on his door. I call loudly.
I pace like a wind-blown reed, but none of my flailing
gets my tools. . . I slip my head under the hood,
cannot wrench a triangle over an oval.
Magic is the tool that fits, taped to the engine.

M. L. Brown/The Wedding Prophet

Inhale the tempest balanced in your tea cup.
Burn in the kettle's steam as you open

a love letter meant for someone else,
lick it shut.   Touch the portent

in the tea leaves, the frilled gills of wonder
on the belly of a mushroom.

You might be the next Cassandra
living in Schenectady   New York.

Snow crackles outside your door at night,
melts with its own motion.

Cassandra might have lied to save her life
but there is no escaping the frog beneath the prince.

You will become her—
everyone will think you mad

as you set your teeth to the edge of the cup,
hear the hem of your wedding dress whisper.

M. L. Brown/Does This Drink Make My Hips Look Big?

Liquid is so light. The right
glass in the hand, a supple flame:
your bones my brain
with the edge off.

Somewhere it's five o'clock,
the sun low enough to pour.
Let me   have one, neat. I know

a girl is supposed to want ice
and umbrellas   something pink
a sling to match her Singapore thong.

Why not fix me one to ease the day after day
that keeps taking a piece of me?

I'm on the west coast but I know
it's evening in the east and
you should love me.

Let's do vodka for breakfast,
                              quick cold
helps a woman
carry her face like a conversation.

I tip the drink, odorless sip,
rim I ride.

Karen Douglass/Go in Disguise

Cold coming on, the sun and
small game burrow deep, not
to be resurrected till spring.

Harvest done, what you've got
is all you'll get. You may yet
trick a neighbor to feed you.

Practice a threat to unlock the pantry,
to make them go below and
bring treats from the root cellar:

"Give this poor dog a bone—
or I boil the dog." Drag
your ragged self, unwashed,

house to house, door to door
selling your poor story; join
the desperate old ones,

hair a fright, eyes red.
They feel beastly, famished,
each waving a cane like a cudgel.

Kevin Clark/Sixties Noir

Smoke means cash, said the stoned collector.
Codie laughed, then paid
The toll with hash. We'd loaned
Ourselves each other, rode
Windowpane down the Jersey summer,
Her face gone jumpin' jack flash,
Her crossroads aura
Sheer as her peasant blouse.

As she twirled the spliff in flame,
I blinked away
The bearded infant narcs
Winking from the starboard wing of the Impala.

By Wildwood, both of us loved
The life we'd worn.
On the starry beach, new friends
Riffed in whispers,
Knew not to Bogart.

Heading home, her same smile
And the turnpike smog
Layered lacquer on my heart. Then,
Visions redux: Altar boys on bennies
Sang the Sanctus in double time.
Cops roved the rearview.
Straight as a line, I couldn't stop
Hallucinating. We drove
The surface roads, said we'd never pay a cent.

Codie held to the wheel, dropped me in Hackensack.
I cracked for good, then headed west.

Maria Fire/Nigredo

—in alchemy, the first phase of the "great work"

Before your name
do you remember the crow?
She cawed to your mother's belly
through that brown wool dress. In steady
staccato bursts she cawed, her claws
tucked, wings snapping. She was your
metronome, urged your folded head and limbs
to liven the beat. Inside your mother's pouch
you tapped passing hours. It was not
your time to ask questions or to hold crow
accountable for strange promises. She
was shouting predictions of carrion and
laughter. Some believe her calling
is what pulled you from that place
where the sun shines black.

Lavonne J. Adams/Cold

1

Frazils: sea ice's first stage—slush crystals textured like the drinks I loved as a kid, cherry and cola that chilled from my mouth's roof to the pale cloud of my forehead.

2

My father was a pilot who took us up in a plane with a wingspan the length of a car. It was December; the heater wasn't working, so the longer we flew, the colder it became. As the engines hummed one long note, as my brother thumbed through a stack of comics, as my sister unbraided and braided her hair, my mother battled with my father over some woman with a beautiful name. I watched what formed on the outside of the window; not quite water, not quite ice. It shaped and reshaped in a code I thought I could understand if I stared persistently, if I refused to avert my eyes. The sky was the muted gray of premonition. After we landed, unable to feel my feet, I stood crying at the top of a hill glazed with ice, afraid to walk, afraid I'd fall.

3

Ablation: a term that evokes sloughing off. As they migrate, glaciers gather debris that is slowly released as it melts, the way we wash our hands or clear our minds, the way we shed snakeskins of pain.

4

At nineteen, I hiked the Blue Ridge Parkway on a March day when flannel shirts felt as cumbersome as blankets. But by nightfall, my fiberfilled sleeping bag seemed as insubstantial as the cotton at the bottom of a gift box. Deep cold shrugged upward from the earth like a hibernating bear awakening, leaving my elbows and knees wracked with chill. Still too weak for warmth, the morning sun glossed each tender leaf, burnished the nearby stream's brisk surface.

5

I once lived in a house where lined curtains and kerosene heaters weren't enough to combat the cold; my children gathered around the small blue ring of flame as if the heater were a campfire. The picture window froze on the inside, as rippled as antique glass. That overlay of coldness distorted vision, formed a panorama of smudged sand and disjointed pines against a pewter Carolina sky.

6

Glaciations: prolonged periods of extreme cold that fringe an ice age.

7

As the Ice Age rumbled in, did Wooly Mammoths lie their heavy bodies down beneath the weight of what they couldn't understand, heart muscles relaxing, sinews and tendons loosening, breathing becoming more and more sluggish as the spin of each molecule slowed like the final vapors rising from their last exhalations?

Lavonne J. Adams/The Tale of Thuridur Formann

In my eleventh year, I was taught
by my father to row—the ache
inside my arms forgotten
as the ocean's currents moved
beneath my skin, my mind mapping
fjords of fish and the trails they followed
through the deep. I am gifted
with *fiskni*, can sense the nearby whales,
know whether they are good or evil.
At home, I wear men's clothing,
sing songs of love to the whales and the fish,
chant to the wind to soothe it before I row.

Still, there is danger when boats heavy
with cod turn back toward the harbor.
My brother Bjarni was like Thor, strong
and resourceful, but the final time he took to sea,
his boat capsized. He swung his hatchet deep
into the hull, used it as a handle to hang on.
The wind and rain were strong adversaries;
from the shore, all we could do was watch.

One by one we are plucked away
even though we mouth prayers,
rub wishing stones, give gifts
of fish heads and roe to the Hidden People.
Each time we turn our boats seaward,
all we have is the strength of our will,
all we own is the moment.

Benjamin J. Van de Griek/Room

That cigarette in the fancy box
looks comfortable.

The dirty leather shoes with the duct tape nose
don't complain.

The cheap Montana guitar
hums sweet tunes about her false origins,

While the dusty old fan pronounces loudly
"It's cool baby."

The old wood table in the center of it all,
sturdy age, draws you into secret history.

A smooth black pen quietly writes—
that's what it does.

A lone, confused hand
bosses it around the always inviting paper,

Trying so hard
not to feel alone.

Paul Lieber/Going In

His neck is longer
this morning and
the profile is almost
a regular thin boy.
He's eleven days
old and he grows
in my arms. There
are grimaces and
silent aches as a finger
stretches. He's
moving toward a thought,
toward a longer leg.
It's all temporary
this unbreakable gaze
between us. Going in
I'm careful with
these looks, too careful,
as if to protect
knowledge of me
he may already have.
This isn't a lesson
or sound philosphy.
It's something
sad, like shyness,
like my mother
refusing a Scotch
or my father
having another.

Lucille Lang Day/Saint James at the Health Museum

It's four o'clock, closing time. *At last I can get some work done*, Cecelia thinks as she approaches the front desk to say good-bye to the volunteers and interns, mostly college students, who are filing out the staff door. But just as the last one leaves, Jim, a street person who stops by from time to time, rushes in. He looks particularly bad today: left eye surrounded with purple bruises and swollen nearly shut, lips puffy and caked with scabs, dark hair hanging in long, greasy strings. His jeans are riddled with holes, his white shirt streaked with dirt and dried blood.

"I've missed you, Cissy," he says, drawing close enough for Cecelia to get a whiff of urine and rancid perspiration that makes her nauseous.

She steps back. "The museum is closed. You'll have to come back during regular hours." She gestures for him to look around the room. The computers, microscopes, light boxes, and displays have been turned off. Only the overhead fluorescent lights remain on, the "warm" variety, giving the room a pinkish hue. She'd like to say, "Don't come back until you clean yourself up. You might scare the children." But the truth is that anyone is allowed in the health museum: it's a public place. The police won't come unless someone is causing trouble, like the time one street person chased another into the museum and started a fistfight. The police refused at first to help when a homeless person decided to take a nap on the sofa. He was there all afternoon, but the police didn't come until closing time, when Cecelia called again, pleading, "Please come get him out of here. He refuses to budge, and I can't leave him here all night."

"I need to talk to you, Cissy. You're the only one who can help me." As Jim speaks, the odor of stale beer slips past his chipped brown teeth, reminding her of past boyfriends and so many mornings after parties when she was younger.

"You look like you've been in a fight."

"I get crazy when I'm drinking. You've never seen me drunk. I'd never come here like that."

"I smell beer."

"But I'm not drunk. After I get drunk, I have to drink again the next day or I get sick. I'm going to quit drinking on November 16."

"Why November 16?"

"It's next Sunday. I want to party one last Saturday night."

"Stopping is a good idea. You can come back here after you do it." She'll get information about AA meetings and other services for alcoholics before he comes again, she tells herself. If he comes back smelling of beer, she'll give him the information and tell him he can't come into the museum anymore until he stops drinking. She resolves to enforce this, even though she's sure the police won't back her up. It would please her to help him; it would make these visits more than an unwelcome interruption.

"No need to say that. I *am* going to stop." He pauses, staring at her. "You're still a beauty queen, you know. You don't have any gray hair."

"I'm old enough to be your mother." She imagines that Jim is about thirty. She's fifty-five, but still slender and agile. It isn't strictly true that she doesn't have any gray hairs. They're just not predominant yet: her honey-colored hair has gradually turned to ordinary brown instead of gray.

"It don't matter. You take care of yourself. I know I shouldn't say this, but I had a dream about making love with you. Please let me touch you." He reaches out with his long, dirty fingers to touch her arm.

Cecelia steps back again, a little too late. "Please don't talk like that. It isn't appropriate. I'm a married woman." She doesn't feel complimented by his attention. If anything, it makes her feel worse about herself and about aging. A man like Jim wouldn't have dared to make a pass at her when she was younger.

When Jim comes on to her, it frightens her. He seems obsessed, and obsession leads to violence. Cecelia's daughter Ali was once preyed upon by Dean, an alcoholic and cocaine addict who'd been her boyfriend. Four years ago, Dean went to Ali's office with a gun after she told him she didn't want to see him anymore. Fortunately, she was out to lunch when he arrived, and one of her coworkers called the police. When Dean pointed his gun at the cops, they shot and killed him. All this happened while Ali was two blocks away, eating a turkey sandwich.

"I had a Tarot reading today," Jim says, "and I asked if I should come see you. The Knight of Cups came up, because I wanted this to be the right time. The last card was the Ace of Swords, which can mean either great prosperity or great misery. I decided to take my chances."

Cecelia wonders how to respond to this nonsense. How can she avoid leading him on or agitating him? She wants to tell him he has to leave now, but she fears his anger. He once gave her a book about natural healing, and she promised to read it. When he came back two weeks later and asked how she liked the book, she said, "I haven't had a chance to read it yet." He went into a rage.

"I hate your guts!" he yelled. "You're nothing but a liar!"

"Calm down," she said. "I really do want to read the book. I just haven't found the time."

"Okay," he said, "I'll give you one more chance." She started reading the book that night and was done two days later, but Jim did not show up again at the museum for almost two years.

Before she says anything, Jim says, "I think we were together in a past life and we'll be together again," his right eyelid twitching, his blue eyes shining. "I been thinking a lot about reincarnation. I been thinking about it so much that I wrote a paper on it. No one in the world could've done a better job than me. Will you make copies?"

Cecelia had made copies of an earlier paper he wrote, "Proof that God Exists." The God paper, which covered such topics as witness of miracles and intelligent design of the universe, briefly allayed her fear of him, because she thought someone religious would feel obligated to keep the Ten Commandments. Then she remembered the Reverend Jim Jones, the religious fanatics who shoot abortion doctors, the priests of the Inquisition. . .

She takes the new paper from his hand. In the upper right corner, it's signed, "James the Flashman." The paper, just one page long, lists twelve types of evidence for reincarnation, each with a brief explanation. "Unusual Birthmarks," "Déjà Vu," and "Strong, Eccentric Interests" catch her eye. She has a birthmark shaped like a butterfly on her inner right thigh, often feels she's been there before when she goes somewhere for the first time, and collects photos, figurines, and souvenirs of all types depicting frogs and toads. For Jim, these things would certainly confirm she was a recycled person. However, she does not believe in reincarnation, astrology, or ghosts. God? She'd like to believe, but the evidence isn't very satisfying. She looks around the museum: at the skeleton, which is missing several finger bones and always appears to be leaning forward; at the heart wall, which is red and white and includes blood pressure equipment and colorful diagrams of the atria, ventricles, and valves; at the giant nerve cell, which is pale green and studded with antler-like dendrites. This is what's real. This is her worldview.

"Do you believe in reincarnation?" he asks, walking toward the drug exhibit.

"Of course," she lies. She has found it best not to argue with irrational people. When her schizophrenic cousin, Joan, warned her that cans with red on the label contain poison, she said, "Thanks for the tip. I'll avoid them." Many mentally ill homeless people have found their way from the street into the museum. Once a paranoid teenage girl with sores all over her face came in and said she had to reprogram all of the computers because the Russians had hooked them up to bombs that were going to explode at midnight on January 1, 2000. Cecelia gave the girl a pad of paper and a pen and said, "The museum is owned by a hospital, and it's against their policy to let anyone except their own programmers work on these computers, but if you write down the reprogramming instructions, I'll see that they do it." The girl sat on the floor by the front desk and wrote furiously for two hours. When she was done, Cecelia looked at the top page, which began "AGA? <> 7540 Lo = 8e7cQ," and thanked the girl profusely. The girl said she had to leave because there were other computers she needed to fix. This was a long time ago, and she hasn't been back since. Then there was the pudgy man with bulging eyes who said that all of the exhibits at the museum were wrong, that there were no such things as germs or DNA damage: all illness was caused by poor relationships with birds, particularly sparrows, finches, and pigeons. If people would talk more to birds and put out feed for them, the birds would protect them, he claimed. Cecelia said, "I'll tell the people who design the exhibits." The man thanked her and left.

"I know who I was in one of my past lives," Jim says. "Want to guess who?" When Cecelia doesn't respond, he adds, "I'll give you a clue: it's someone important in the Bible."

He's standing in front of the reaction timer, staring at a photograph of a young girl on a skateboard. Cecelia considers taking him to the other side of the drug exhibit to show him the lumpy, green cirrhotic liver but decides not to, because she doesn't want to prolong his visit.

"Jesus?" she says. It occurs to her that a combined homicide and suicide might not seem wrong to someone who believes in reincarnation. This might seem like a logical option if you want to hurry yourself and someone else along to a better life. The idea of a better life makes her think of Darin, her boyfriend in college. If she'd stayed with him, she wouldn't be in a closed museum in Chico today with a crazy man. She would have had a different life, maybe better. She would have been spared the marriage to Russell, the neurotic chemistry teacher who made her miserable for fourteen years. How odd that one decision changes everything! She tells herself that Darin might have turned out to be as insufferable as Russell if she'd married him, but she can't make herself believe it. He fixed waffles for breakfast on Sunday mornings and always held her hand when they watched a movie, even if it was only on television. More importantly, there was none of the passive-aggressive stuff that Russell put her through. Darin would say so when something was wrong. Oh well, she thinks, at least she has a loving husband now.

"No, but that's close. I was Saint James!" Jim's blue eyes, somehow familiar, send out piercing rays of light.

"Which one?" She has read the Bible and knows that three Jameses in the New Testament were later declared saints: James, the Lord's brother; James, son of Zebedee, one of the twelve apostles; and James, son of Alphaeus, another apostle.

"Son of Zebedee."

"He's the one who was beheaded."

"I asked for a place of honor, but was promised only a share in Christ's sufferings," Jim says, showing that he's read the Gospels. He sighs. "It was a test, and the Lord is still testing me."

We're both being tested, Cecelia thinks.

She heads toward the copy machine in the staff room, and Jim follows. "I can't keep doing this for you," she says, setting the machine to make twenty copies. "If my boss at the hospital finds out, I'll get in trouble. You have to stop drinking and get a job."

"I know. I'll be a DJ. I know more about music than anyone. I'll call all the radio stations. Do you think I can do it?"

"Yes, if you stop drinking."

She walks back to the front desk before handing him the copies. When he opens his crusty green backpack to put them inside, he pulls out a mesh bag. He opens it, saying, "I brought you a present," and takes out a small book, *The Yoga Sutras of Patanjali*. "I paid eight dollars for it."

Cecelia hesitates, then takes the book. "I want you to read it," he says. "I wouldn't lead you wrong. The natural-healing book was good, wasn't it?"

She nods, knowing she is going deeper into a place where she doesn't want to go.

"What did you like best in it?"

"The case histories of the people who healed themselves." She has told him this before. Cecelia does believe in the body's regenerative and self-healing powers, but she doesn't think this is enough to overcome all illness.

Jim nods. "Wasn't that awesome? Especially the woman who had cancer."

He gives her back the original of the paper on reincarnation. "I want you to make copies and give them to your husband, your daughters, and all your friends. I'll post it on bulletin boards and telephone poles, even though hostile people will come along and take it down, like they did my paper on God. I think it's the students and professors who take my work down. They're jealous because they can't write as good as me. They just don't have the ideas."

He puts on his backpack. Cecelia is relieved.

He takes it off again and pulls out a bottle of gingko pills. "I take this every day for energy. I only been taking it for one week, and I already feel much better. I want you to take it too."

"I don't have a problem with energy."

"That don't matter. You'll feel much better. I want you to take it, and every day we can compare how we feel."

"I have a lot of allergies, so I don't take anything unless I have to."

"This won't give you allergies. It's herbal!"

"So is poison oak."

"That's different. They don't put it in bottles and sell it."

"I've had bad reactions to both valerian and evening primrose oil, which they do put in bottles and sell."

"You should at least try it," he says, handing her the information sheet that came with the pills. "It might help you." As she takes the tightly folded piece of paper from him, she notices his ring, which is silver and turquoise. The piece of turquoise is unusual: a large, triangular stone with a zigzag red streak that looks like a lightning bolt. It is just like the stone in a ring she gave Darin.

"I have to get back to work," she says, wondering how he could have a ring so similar to Darin's.

"I got nothing to do. Can I watch you work?"

"No, that would make me uncomfortable." She opens the gingko sheet and pretends to read it, her heart beating very fast, as he puts his pack back on. She has gotten through one more encounter with Jim, but she is disgusted with herself for letting this go on for three years. She thought he would disappear, like the computer girl and the bird man, but this is no longer a reasonable expectation. She will have to get information on alcohol and drug rehabilitation programs—and chew out the staff for letting Jim in at closing time. But first she must find out about the ring, which looks exactly like the one she bought for Darin on Telegraph Avenue in Berkeley from the jewelry designer who made it.

She takes a deep breath. "Nice ring." She tries to sound casual.

"It was my father's."

Suddenly, she feels dizzy and queasy. Although it's unlikely that Darin is Jim's father, now that the possibility has arisen, she can't simply dismiss it. The air is dissected into small shards of colored glass as she tries to focus on Jim's face. "Are you close to him?" Her voice has a quaver that she can't suppress. She's angry at herself for feeling such grief over something that's probably just an odd coincidence, and she's angry at Jim for being the vehicle of this coincidence. At the same time, her grief is greater than her anger.

"He died of a heroin overdose in 1982. He was wearing this ring when he died."

"I'm so sorry." She sobs, biting her lip, looking away from him. This is totally ridiculous, she tells herself. Darin is probably fine. Even if it is his ring, it was probably stolen from him.

"Don't feel bad, Cissy. My mom and him separated when I was four. I hardly knew him."

When she finally looks at Jim, his right eyelid is twitching again. The blue eyes, so similar to Darin's. "You're *still* a beauty queen," he says as he leaves.

She stands very still, wanting to rush after him, throw her arms around him, and tell him everything will be okay from now on, but she knows this isn't true. Wondering what Darin would want her to do, whether or not Jim is his son, she walks slowly to her office, letting her tears flow.

The computer screen on her desk is blue: a deep lake, a birdless sky. Blue like Jim's eyes, like Darin's. She can see Darin's eyes and resolute jaw very clearly. What became of him? Could he have become addicted to heroin? There must be many triangular pieces of turquoise with red zigzags in this world, she tells herself. She should have asked Jim his last name and his father's name, and she should have asked him to take off the ring and show it to her. Darin's ring had an inscription: "C.S. loves D.F." It would have been so easy to clarify everything! But no matter how small the likelihood that Darin was Jim's father, she could not have risked proving it. She could not have endured it.

She looks out her office window at the body systems and safety exhibits. There is no point in trying to concentrate on vitamins, minerals, macronutrients, and calories—the grant proposal she should be writing for a new nutrition exhibit. She can't work. Can she do more for Jim? Who knows? She starts to weep for all the things one loses—childhood, lovers, friends, parents, opportunities, one's youthful body, finally even memories and life itself. Opening *The Yoga Sutras of Patanjali* at random, she reads, "As a flawless crystal absorbs what is placed before it, so the settled mind is transparent to whatever it meets—the seer, the process of seeing, or the object seen," and wonders if her own mind will ever be that clear.

William Archila/Late April, 1939

Mr. Levine & me lean against the rail
in this black and white photograph, hats
tipped back, dressed in our best suits,
vests with a watch chain across the belly.

It's a saloon on a dark street, downtown,
years of alcohol, sweat and grime,
construction workers, rough
as the bricks they laid, their laughter

a great clapper of tongues. We were back
from a war from which no one returned
the same as they'd left,
where simple men become generals,

and the dust of the Holy Ghost gathers
in the breath of deep sleep. We belong
in this photograph the size of a soapbox,
feeling the burn ease down our throats,

cigarette smoke scattered like crowns
falling apart in the light. Here we stay
with the bruised air of olives, the dry
sound of earth risen in our bones,

with the bluesman and his ivories, his head
rested over the keys. I don't remember
who held the camera, but I remember
stepping into the coal dust of dawn,

loving the way our shoes bent
as we walked, hammering that song
for those who fell without a hole, a shovel
full of soil known only to Spain.

Anemone Beaulier/The October Shore

You stop the car in a lot overlooking
a vacant beach. The moon is pressing

through the slit between sky and sea,
pointing an orange finger across the dark water.

We are silent, as we have been since we knew
we were lost: a wrong turn miles back.
Silent, as we have been for months.

This drive to a seaside inn, so we might find words. . .
There's only more silence: a road twisting

beneath bare trees, the boarded-up windows
of an empty cottage. The map lies
in the back seat, of no use, we are so lost.

We watch the moon contract into an ashen fist,
redrawing the world in black and white:
its pale light makes ghosts of your hands.

The only sound is sand rasping against
the car, blown by a rising wind.

Anemone Beaulier/The Effete Arithmetic

I count: twenty-one days, twenty-one pills; then seven days,
seven saccharin placebos.
Estrogen and progestin in rows like candy: peach, blush,
lavender, jonquil. I count:
twenty-four days between each four days of bleeding. I count
when I am late: the six days
in Manassas that rainy August, those four days last March
when the robins flocked and sang,
a month that winter I was so sick. Seven days today.
My stomach turns, and I think
I feel a baby's heart flutter. Palm to stomach, I count:
the years I've loved my husband,
the years on these pills, the years left for us to have a child.
I count the long weeks we've lost
to fighting, the days I've lost in bed. But I cannot say
what I want. Not yet. Not yet.

Anna Leahy/At the Ore Dock

Marquette, Michigan

The ore dock chutes let down
like teats to fill the ship's belly with pellets.
I think of this likeness only
because a friend has just had a C-section,
her daughter feeds in clusters,
and I rush toward infertility.
Or I think of it because my sister's dog
has just had more puppies than it has teats
and I wonder why the bitch jumps the fence for more.
The chutes look like chorus-line legs.

But the dock is a masculine thing,
I finally admit, all concrete and iron,
a heavy structure stomped down at the shore.
A chute, then, is more phallus than teat or leg,
and the dock, a row, one after the other hanging down.
Atop the ore dock, the train, a string of cars
like holiday lights or a necklace—
but railroad cars are not delicate things.
I look to the smooth curve of wheel to rail.

The cars tip, the chutes fill, the ore makes
a racket in the torrential rush
as the ship sinks to its watermark,
accepting its fill before leaving.

Robert Funge/Deception

Never to be deceived.
What a dull life.
Tell me lies.

Praise my intellect
before you tell me
what you need.

Just don't be honest.
Truth sobers,
and I like being drunk

on possibilities.
Don't tell me
orchids won't grow

in my garden of weeds.
It's an illusion
I could believe,

like the girl of my dreams,
in a dream,
even when I know

it's a dream.
Truth corrupts
the imagination,

so lie to me.
Tell me you accept what I do.
Tell me I'm good.

Robert Funge/Stars

Between supper at *Stars* and the concert
at Davies Hall, there's the usual
walk down Van Ness. An old man
holds a sign asking that I feed his dog.
A woman whose eyes are still beautiful
offers to take me in her mouth
if I will feed her. And a young man
whose name changes each time we talk

is reading Vonnegut, lost
on the planet Titan. Now his name
is Chrono, and he's waiting
for his father. A dollar in his hat
can't bring him back to earth. An old woman
sits under a blanket on the steps
of the Opera House. I give her a dollar,
and my coat feels cold.

The meal was fine. A plate of bruschetta,
Pollo Toscana and a glass
of chardonnay. The modern music
bored me, but Yo Yo Ma
did more than justice to Frank.
His cello wept my tears.
A comfortable ride home, a small port
with Mussorgsky, a warm bed.

I try to fantasize myself
in worn-out clothes, sitting with a dog
on a street corner, being hungry
outside a restaurant. I can't take their pain
on or away. I try to sleep,
but look up at the ceiling
and wonder what it's like to be cold
in a distant world, under a roof of stars.

Sarinea Meserkhani/Perfection, Unattainable; Vanity, Inevitable

you are not beautiful, despite what *Vogue* and *Cosmo* say.
your superficial good looks come from a compact and brush,
not the DNA your parents so graciously passed down to you.
you buff way your flaws, fill your pores with liquid
two shades too dark for your imperfect skin.
blend them away and maybe they'll cease to exist.
blend too hard, and maybe you'll cease to exist.
you can only ask for so much.
polish, paint, smooth, scrape.
confidence in a bottle; what a concept!
but you're not confident, you little wench,
not even with your mask.
deep inside you ache in the hollows of your shell.
you weep so deep beneath the surface,
no one can hear your wails of desperation.
cry in your corner, you superficial bitch;
you'll never amount to anything.
snort that line of precious white,
maybe then you'll find true happiness.
inject bliss into your arm and cover up
the bruises that euphoria left as a memento.
paste that artificial smile on your face,
hope it doesn't shatter.
glue on your false eyelashes,
pout your "passion pink" lips,
maybe then somebody will love you.
as you strive for perfection
you only get further and further from it,
until you fade away a fabricated, deceitful lie.
that's all you ever were,
that's all you ever will be.

Barbara F. Lefcowitz/Typhoid Mary

They accused Typhoid Mary of murder
though she did not mean to kill a single soul
did not know she carried a deadly bacillus inside her.
She claimed she baked her puddings and cakes
from the best ingredients in New York.

It's not what what you cooked,
the Health Department said, but you,
your hands, your blood, your breath.
Had anyone those days heard of DNA
surely they would have mentioned that too.

The rest of her life she was quarantined
in a remote and solitary cabin. Just a poor
Irish immigrant with no schooling
she didn't think to say
that everything born carries death

in its bonework inner basket. . .
every bird, lion, fish or tree.
Likely it would have made
scant difference, like everyone else
her accusers kept such thoughts at bay

believed they would live forever, like all those gods
created as models, believed they carried only good
and joyful things in those other baskets,
the ones they slung across their backs
as they sauntered whistling through the woods.

Barbara F. Lefcowitz/The Eyes of Darkness

On dark windy nights green traffic lights dance as if drunk.
Darkness is to gestation as light is to birth.
The medieval bone-dancers are dark furrows in Hell's woodcuts.
My efforts to learn the Danse Macabre are thus premature.
The pain of giving birth is milder than the pain of getting born.
Coal tumbling down a chute made an oddly comforting sound.
Who licked the frosting off the black-and-white cakes of my youth?
I caught a snowflake and dried it to find its black core of dust.
Queen Victoria wore only jet brooches after the Prince died.
Do you have Prince Albert in a can? Let him out, for god's sake.
The eyes of darkness are upon you. All the live-long day.
Unlike its cousin The Charleston, the Black Bottom sounds racist.
The black diamond in my palm turned white in the lamplight.
Soon the blueblack-cold night of the soul will become spilled ink.

William P. O'Brien/After the Flame-Out

(Bill Woods, Arthur Roth, Kenny Street)

Off they went like Icarus
into their wild blue yonderings
climbing high into a sun so dazzling
we forgot about the waxed feathers.

And how we envied them
as they droned in by night
over searchlight-slashed cities
to be met by pom-pom flowers
with petals of flame.

Even in death they dazzled us.
They flamed out like meteors
in the presence of constellations;
they scattered like star seeds on the
Elysian fields—or so it seemed in
the freshman class at Flushing High.

But now we see them in a different light—
in the scalpel ray of sun on a winter afternoon,
        before the first incision;
in the heat lightning of a summer evening,
        with all the nerves exposed;
in the incandescence of the back porch light—
and with the stunned silence of moths.

Cammy Thomas/Hem of Your Garment

When I last saw you
the garment was a thin sheet,
your face a balloon,
blood still flowing, heart thumping
to the machines.
The blow opened your skull—
just the war of life,
the car, the truck, the soft mystery of the body,
torso untouched under the sheet,
still firm and shapely,
fingers on the covers wiped off but bloody.

Jesus gave me water
but I could not kneel to wash you.
Your body went to be burned—
sweet bone we will release you
to that water you love,
that lasting water,
that ash on the mountain.

Joseph Levens/Scorpion

My twin stepsisters, Reckless and Ruthless, are going to the beach. Their real names are Nora and Ethel, and their mother is Virginia, but for practical purposes I refer to the twins by nickname, and the mother by a token which suits her best: Psycho.

Anyway, R & R tell me they are bored. We are lounging on the veranda overlooking the ocean in our villa on St. John, between college semesters. After letting on about where they went last night, one of them says, "That's it. Let's go down to the water. I can't take the heat."

Of course, I have every intention of following—there's not much else to do here in the happy Caribbean—and I ask what beach they had in mind.

"The one you can walk to," says Ruthless, truthfully. "By yourself."

Let me tell you something about Ruthless. She's the one with the dark hair. She can make any man feel about the size and shape of a dinner pea. And not one of those tasty French peas in the can with the shiny silver label. We're talking one sorry frozen thing that comes in a plastic bag with corn and carrots, shriveled up like the life was sucked out of it as it tried to get away. I've never met a more direct, abrasive individual. If you'd like to meet her and get social, I suggest you start off slowly, with email or instant messenger.

"Will we need an umbrella?" I ask.

"Definitely," says Ruthless. "Be sure to bring it."

The two are wearing red bikini bottoms, skimpy little things that they are proud of, as our feet knock along wooden planks. There is no wind today and the sun beats down on us like a club. A thicket of fanning palms is to our sides, lining the walk. These boards are hard but I have this feeling I'm going to get splinters. I guess there's nothing I can really do about it since my flip-flops are out of commission. Psycho's beagle urinated on them on the deck last night, the bastard. Where is Psycho anyway? She's been gone all day. I ask the girls this.

"She's with *Mikel*," says Reckless, turning around, putting the flats of her hands against each other and leaning the side of her head into them.

"They slept together?" I say.

I should know better than to ask Reckless this question. Forensic science will find fascinating particles under the girl's fingernails, I'm sure, many of which may only have reached there the night before. And as for Psycho, nothing surprises me anymore. My stepmother left my eccentric father years ago, and I'm sorry to report that I've been with her ever since. She's run the gamut and I often times compare her to that line about New York City: "Anything you can imagine happening between people, and more, happens in New York, and probably all of it at this very moment."

To clarify, though, I've come to know and love my stepfamily. We've grown into a close, cozy foursome, with me the only one with shoes large enough to kill crawling insects in our apartment off Central Park East.

"Something reeks," says Ruthless, and she stops in her tracks. The three of us freeze. To the side of the path and in the underbrush we see the shell of a scorpion. Flying insects buzz around it.

"Ain't that the life of the party," says Ruthless.

"One of your dates from last night," I say.

We look at the dead creature a moment. Its translucent orange color certainly makes it appear it could pack a wallop of a bite.

"They say scorpions always travel in pairs," I say, to add some afternoon drama.

R & R shiver. Their feet stomp in place. They hold their arms tight against their sides. I can see goose bumps on their breasts, their nipples hard and alarmed, even though it's hot as hell.

"You're such an idiot moron," says Ruthless. "Why don't you just go back up to the house, drop those pathetic jams, and play with yourself." She takes her sister by the hand and continues down the path to the sparkling shoreline.

The stinger of the dead scorpion points to the sky like a miniature rocket launcher. I look at it a moment as the thumping of the girls' walk fades away and all that is left is the buzzing of the circling insects. I can reach in and take the shell if I want, and add it to my box of collectibles back home. Maybe on the way back that's what I'll do.

❖❖❖

So it seems Psycho will be gone for dinner. We haven't heard from her all day. Reckless is a little bit concerned. She had met this fellow Mikel in town a few days ago and introduced him to her mother over evening cocktails. He kissed Psycho's hand. And it wasn't a Hi-How-are-you-Pleased-to-meet-you kiss, it was one that clearly demonstrated his intention: "I'm going to screw your daughter tonight. Thank you so much for bringing her into this world and visiting my little town. And if there is anything I can do for you, please don't hesitate." I actually didn't see the kiss, but this is Reckless' report, and I have no reason to dispute its veracity.

"It looks like he treated *you* all right," I say. "I see you're still in one piece."

"Mom's not me. She's twenty years older," says Reckless.

"If she agrees to a date with someone half her age, she can take responsibility for whatever happens."

Reckless isn't listening to me. She's playing with all the little beads hanging down off her shoulders. After returning from the beach a few hours ago, my stepsisters decided to do this *hair project* they'd been talking about ever since the airline flight. Now it's complete and she seems happy with the results. I must admit, the beads do look pretty nice. They're a mixture of bright red, orange, and yellow, fastened to the bottoms of sun-streaked braids of blonde.

"Why didn't you do your sister's hair like she did yours?" I ask.

"She didn't want them. And besides, I don't know what the hell I'm doing when it comes to that," she says.

Ruthless is in the kitchen and I think she's pissed off. No Psycho means no dinner, and she's probably wondering what to do. Although she may be just as concerned about her mother, Ruthless, I'm sure, has been thinking about the pate and creole in the refrigerator, but she doesn't know how to cook or reheat.

And, speaking of the angel, here she is.

"So, what are we doing?" Ruthless asks, her palms flat on the side table separating us.

"Should we wait for her?" Reckless looks up.

"No," I blurt out. "Gallows Point has filet mignon tonight. I'm going there. And I'm not waiting half an hour for the two of you to make up your minds." Impatience is one of my vices, one of the things genetically handed down to me by my father. As with most other things the man might have done for me, I'm not very thankful for it. Sometimes, I get in trouble because of this trait. I hurled a vase through a mirror in a fit of rage last year after waiting fifteen minutes for sales service at a Macy's counter and being completely ignored. I don't wish to discuss the events that ensued.

"You're not taking the Jeep," says Ruthless.

"I'll walk," I say, folding my arms. "It's a nice night."

I already know what's going to happen. After a few moments in the living room listening to other suggestions and ideas, I'll say, "That's it. See you," and as I head out the door I'll hear, "Wait. We're coming. Just let us throw something on." So I'll turn around and wait for them, and we'll find that in half an hour they'll finally be decent and reaching for their satchels. I'm telling you, they treat me like crap, but they really can't live without me. The sad part is that they don't even realize this.

❖❖❖

Leave it to R & R to bring sweat to the forehead of our short and stubby waiter from Cuba or Cancun or Cozumel. They ask him if fresh spinach leaves are used in the salad. They ask where the olives came from. Soon we find we have a different waiter, a tall, native island inhabitant, and now the spinach and the olives and whether or not we will be given chilled forks become unimportant, and they want to know if he likes to swim in lighted pools after midnight.

He's got an answer for every question and talks about things others would not expect. You might think he'd give compliments on the braids and beads, on the jewelry, the animated outfits, any fine detail having to do with the way R & R appear, but no, not with words. This is all a language communicated discreetly and inconspicuously. He sees every feature of my twin stepsisters and conveys his appreciation in a way I have difficulty understanding, but nonetheless know is there. I can see it in all of their expressions—the eyes on one another, the half-smiles.

"I'm Nora and I'm having the filet mignon, medium rare, thank you," says Reckless, chin up.

"And I'm Ethel and I'm having the Pasta Carbonara, thank you," says Ruthless.

"I'll have the broiled jumbo shrimp please," I add.

"And you are. . . ?" The waiter's dynamic personality is just to die for.

"Amarjit."

"I'm Giorgio," says the waiter. "I'll be right back with your salads." He turns and leaves.

"Amarjit?" asks one of them.

"Shrimp?" asks the other.

"You know that scorpion we saw while walking to the beach?" I say to them.

"What about it?" they respond in unison.

"It's under your pillow."

"Cut it out," says Ruthless. "What are we going to do about Mom? She's gotten out of control lately. What's with her?"

Reckless looks across the table and can see her sister's concern. There's something about twins. It's like they each have their own body but they share the same state of being, as if a single force drives both of them. I read in the newspaper about two twin brothers on Long Island who once bowled perfect games the same night in different towns. It's just one of those things, I guess.

"You know, if she did something stupid I'm going to let her have it," says Ruthless. "What kind of person was this *Mikel* anyway?"

"He was all right," says Reckless, "The one thing that scares me, though, is he looked like he had no limits. The kind of person who would do anything and everything."

"Trouble," mumbles Ruthless.

This conversation just cracks me up. I'm sorry, I know we're talking about a missing mother, but listen to these two. They just met this guy a few days ago, and one of them probably satisfied his every wish. It's hard for me to accept their concern about someone else when it seems so obvious they aren't too concerned about themselves. I don't know how they're getting by in psychology and sociology. I'm pulling my hair out in electrical engineering, and I'm the one who has to look out for these two.

When the salad arrives, Reckless has another question for our waiter, but I don't know what it is because she calls him close and whispers in his ear. The man Giorgio smiles unequivocally.

"We're looking for our mother," I say.

Ruthless turns to me abruptly.

"She's flirting, you idiot." She hits me in the side with her elbow and gives me beaming eyes.

Giorgio looks up at me, still wearing the smile. His teeth are clean and white but his eyes are bloodshot and sleepy.

"She's got long, red hair," I say, "and green eyes and she's tall and skinny and she's probably wearing an outlandish dress. Maybe even a hat with fake flowers or fruit." I want to tell him she's a victim of old money, but don't.

"I'll take a look around, my friend," says Giorgio.

Reckless pulls the waiter's arm and throws one more thing in his ear, and apparently it is funny because they both giggle. He leaves us, his happy, bouncing, feeble gait too bright for a place like this, but I guess that's what happens when a woman wearing a scanty little skirt tells you she wants to meet you later on. Let's face it, they weren't trading prize-winning recipes or their favorite places to surf cast.

"Isn't that slit on the skirt you're wearing a little too high?" I ask Reckless.

"It's not a skirt," she replies. "It's a sarong."

"Aren't sarongs longer?" I persist.

Ruthless, who happens to be wearing exactly the same thing, delivers a response too vulgar for me to repeat.

After dinner, the three of us split up. Ruthless takes the Jeep and heads back, claiming she is just too tired to do anything. We can all guess where Reckless has chosen to go—nowhere. She's in the kitchen of the restaurant with Giorgio, or maybe in the pantry or walk-in refrigerator.

I decide to make my way back to the villa on foot. The night is hot, but not unbearably so. I've done it before; the walk is peaceful. I can hear crickets and some other creatures making snapping noises hidden in shrubbery along red clay paths.

I cut through a few resorts, each one having elaborate lighted walkways and overhanging palm trees. I don't know how they get these low voltage lights to stay quiet. The ones my father has at his home buzz real loud and annoy the hell out of me. He keeps saying nothing can be done about it.

I pass a few guests as I go, most of whom are barefoot, wearing white. They all smile, happy to greet me. There's a couple, about sixty, walking slowly, holding hands, saying nothing. There's another considerably younger that may be on their honeymoon. Also holding hands, their arms swing between them like a pendulum. And, of course, I see a few small families, some who are complete, some of whom have one parent missing. I can tell they all are just as spoiled as we are. I wonder if they have cooks in their villas. That's the next thing we need.

A mother and her son and daughter are walking ahead of me in the same direction. They aren't saying much. The mother's wearing a white dress with a sheer outer layer falling from her waist. Her wavy, frosted hair lies on her shoulders as if it's been fastened with Velcro, precisely the reason the daughter's hair is rebelliously long and dark and straight. The son is wearing a creme sports jacket and khaki slacks rolled above the ankle. He holds his shoes leisurely behind the nape of his neck, something his father probably taught him, but now his father is in Las Vegas or Paris, perhaps, with a mistress. Or maybe he's divorced like mine, almost out of the picture completely. My father said to me one night a long time ago, "Jeff, Virginia's a good mother. She looks cheap and easy but she'll be there when you need her. And Mom—God bless her loving soul—would have been there also." Inspiring words to live by, wouldn't you say?

My father was right about Psycho being cheap and easy, and it's likely I'll be able to prove it in the next few minutes. Walking into our driveway I see the queen has finally returned, the Alfa Romeo parked with one wheel in the planter.

The bright red scarf lying near the vehicle is the first clue of something going on. I stumble on the doorstep and hear giggling through the front bedroom window—my stepmother's room. She obviously has a guest, and the guest doesn't have his own wheels. Great.

In the foyer there's a Polaroid face down on the ceramic tile. I pick it up and there she is—Psycho in a white print dress with the missing red accessory. She happens to be taking off her sandals in the photo, balanced on one foot and smiling for the camera.

In the living room are several more Polaroids spread about the floor: Psycho holding a bottle of champagne, Psycho showing some leg, Psycho bending forward with puckered lips like Marilyn Monroe without the birthmark and platinum hair.

The giggles continue and the photos are like a breadcrumb trail to the bedroom and I hesitate picking up any more. Instead, I knock on my stepsisters' door and Ruthless answers it calmly, letting me in.

"She's such an asshole," she says, motioning to the other room. She turns and walks back over to the window. I lie on Reckless' bed face up, my hands on my chest, patting it with my fingers.

"How's your headache?" I ask, trying to be a little compassionate.

"I don't have a headache," she says cynically. "Did I *say* I had a headache?"

"You left so quick. I thought you didn't feel well."

Ruthless releases a sigh. "I'm just tired, all right?" she says, looking away from me, out the window.

There aren't any lights on in the room. The moon casts a narrow parallelogram of light on the floor. I can't say for sure what my stepsister is wondering about. Standing by the window of the dark room, her body and mind are in silhouette.

The tips of my fingers pat against my ribs and I develop a rhythm. They tap to a tune I heard yesterday played by a street rat on his kettledrums. It was a charming rendition of a song from my childhood, and for a fraction of a second brought me back to a time when life was baseball cards and bubble gum.

"Remember when you stole my New York Mets yearbook?" I ask Ruthless.

"What?" she says, still facing the window.

"My New York Mets yearbook," I say. "Remember when you stole it and showed it to your boyfriend, telling him it was yours?"

"So?" she says, uninterested.

"You know, I could have walked right on in and told him it was *my* yearbook, that you didn't know the first thing about baseball, that you hated it when I used to hog the big TV and watch the game. I could have done that, you know, but I didn't. I let you fool him."

"Are you saying you want me to come over there and suck your dick or something?"

"I'm just recalling the old days," I say. "Back then, we didn't know anything. I didn't know about Virginia. I didn't know your dad, you didn't know mine. None of it seemed to matter much. What mattered to us was whether the Mets would make it to the World Series and whether your boyfriend would ask you to a movie or a dance. That's all that mattered."

No response from Miss Ruthless, and I think my words might have been heard.

We hear a car pull into the dirt outside. Both of us stop, turn, look into the living room. The front door opens and Reckless shows Giorgio in quietly. We can see them tread along the floor on tiptoes until they approach our open door. Ruthless reaches for a robe.

"Ethel?" Reckless whispers. She hears light laughter coming from the other bedroom and giggles herself, turning to glance at Giorgio. "Ethel?" she says again in the dark, "Is that Mom?"

"It's her," I say. "She's with someone."

"Where's Ethel?" she asks me, looking in my general direction.

"I'm right here," says Ruthless.

"Oh," says Reckless.

"Hi Giorgio," I say.

"You found your mother," he replies. His attempt to comfort excels.

"Listen, brother. . . ," says Reckless, "are you going back out?"

"Yeah, yeah," I reply, "I'm way ahead of you. Go ahead, take my room. I'll sleep here."

❖❖❖

Some sort of animal is making its way through the thicket behind our house. I can hear dried weeds rustle and crack. It could be a night predator; who the hell knows what they have down here. I'm used to seeing possum and skunk and raccoon when we go camping in the woods upstate. Maybe it's a snake or something. Wouldn't that be news.

I look to the window. I don't think anything will be able to make its way inside and the threat doesn't bother me. The crackling noise does, however, as well as all the other damn clamor I am hearing. I'm never going to be able to get some sleep. In the bed beside me Ruthless breathes heavily. Her dark hair is flung out in so many different directions she's got to be having a nightmare. I can see the sweat on her body in the moonlight. I'm thinking about waking her up, taking her out of her needless misery and sending her into a calmer state.

In the next room Psycho is still at it. In the other room more of the same. I already had to kick the wall once, telling them to shut the fuck up.

❖❖❖

Evidently the night was a success for most of us. The four lovebirds in the house all want to have breakfast on the deck. It's ten o'clock and it looks like it's going to be another hot and sunny day in paradise.

I thought Mikel would have been the first to leave. Why would a young guy want to stick around with a woman who could pass for his mother? But then I remember that he has no ride and I guess Psycho just isn't in the mood to drive him home or ask one of us to do it. So here he is, all smiles and curious to know where the food is.

Reckless and Giorgio are holding hands, how nice. The only time they're apart is when they need to use the bathroom. Once again, an uncommon thing to happen—Reckless' man hanging around the next morning. I'm at a loss to justify this exception. Maybe later I'll ask her about it.

At the breakfast table I bring up the idea of getting a cook. The women raise their brows. The three of them look to each other as if they're team members on a game show, just having been shown the prize they will win if they answer the jackpot question correctly.

Psycho says, "I suppose I can check in town and get a good name, so that the next time we come down here we have this luxury."

None of us press the issue farther. When Psycho says something positive, we leave it be and dangle it over her head when the time comes—a strategy that's been proven to work.

It's no surprise that the two men at the table have nothing to say. This is more than a breakfast, it's a family meeting. Or at least I have the feeling it will turn into one.

"Mom," Ruthless says, "we were going to wait for you for dinner last night, but we had no idea where you were."

"Silly, I told you I had a date," Psycho responds, smiling heartily at Mikel.

"You didn't tell us anything," Ruthless argues. "We were at the beach all afternoon. Did you leave us a note?"

"Oh, daughter," Psycho says with a wave of the hand, "you take things too seriously. Lighten up, will you? We're on vacation."

I look at my stepmother and can sense myself getting annoyed.

"You know," I say, "you did have these two crybabies a little worried."

Psycho gives a sinister snicker and raises her coffee mug to her mouth, but some unidentifiable force suddenly causes me to grab it before it reaches her lips. I hold it in place, my one hand over the two of hers. I don't know exactly what it is that made me just do this, but now that I've done it, it feels pretty good. Her face is a registry of shock and she doesn't know how to react. She quickly becomes embarrassed in the company of our two male friends, her face as flushed as a bad sunburn. Before she can say anything, Mikel is up and informing us he needs to meet someone in town. He walks off. Giorgio glances over at Reckless.

I'm still holding the mug and I know I'm not going to get any helpful support from the stepsisters. I also know too well the source of all those infamous traits they possess, a source that can be difficult to reckon with sometimes, and I think I'll pass on dealing with it this sunny morning. I retract my hand, stand, place my napkin gently on the table, and head for the sliding door into the villa.

❖❖❖

There's a boy with his father walking up from the beach. They both wear towels around their waists. Their hair and skin are dark and wet.

It's early afternoon and I'm on my way down to the water. Yesterday, the sand and the ocean and the shade under the trees were just too good. The little beach at the end of our road is one of the island's best kept secrets, probably the reason we have our villa situated here.

"Look at that scorpion, Dad," says the boy, as I approach them. They both stop on the wooden path and peer into the undergrowth. The boy stoops and points. The father looks to me briefly as I pass, smiling and nodding. Then he faces his son.

I pause for a moment and gaze in with them, standing next to the boy. I try to imagine myself this young person and his life, never quite knowing for sure what such a thing is like.

"It looks scary," the boy says.

"That's a pretty big one," says the father. "Good thing he's dead."

The boy nods.

The father runs his fingers over the top of his son's head, messing up his hair, a display of affection foreign to me, yet seeming so natural and ordinary. Before continuing up the path, the father and son smile at me one more time.

At the shoreline, I see R & R have already gone into the ocean once; their hair is damp, their nipples small, brown, and shriveled. I sometimes want to ask them why they openly display themselves like this while covering up without fail back in the New York apartment. Maybe it's simply the wretched Caribbean bliss. If they were to modify their practice, I'm not sure which I'd prefer.

Lying down, the suntan lotion on their skin is a sheen of white, its glimmer blinding. I thought they said Giorgio would be joining us, but looking around I don't see him.

"Where's the waiter?" I ask Reckless.

They both look up at me, shading their eyes.

"What did you bring?" Ruthless asks.

"Rum, of course."

"With ice?" Reckless asks.

"What am I, a servant?" I say.

My stepsisters sit up and face me. It's obvious there are no other men in the picture right now. If there were, I wouldn't be given this much attention.

I reach into the straw bag I lugged with me and pull out a colorful beach towel. I'll lie next to them for a while, until I can't take the sun anymore. Then I'll spread out under a sea grape tree and read or sleep. I don't know how they can stay all day in the scorching sun. It just drains all my energy, the same way a strong hot shower does.

After I'm settled, I retrieve from the same bag cocktail glasses for the three of us. We're not sloppy drunks, at least not as bad as someone else we know. One of Psycho's favorite lines to a bartender: "Make it a double, and spill a little in the glass, will you, darling?"

Well, I'm not spilling any here in this weather. This stuff is strong and can ruin the evening if we're not careful. I'll control myself and pour modest measures.

"You really got her this morning," Ruthless says as she holds out her glass. "I mean, did you see her? She was stifled. It was classic."

A rare pat on the back from a woman who normally uses a knife. I should feel so privileged.

Reckless agrees. She doesn't say anything but I can tell by her expression. Looking at the rum as it flows, I'm sure she's happily awaiting the next high, the next exciting episode of her vacation. She should keep a diary. People would pay top dollar to read it.

We raise our glasses in a toast, a salute. The sound of them clinking seems out of place for a beach, seems more fitting in a room or balcony set with tables and chairs and candles. The intoxicant is warm and cutting and causes us to wince.

"Did you bring any fruit?" asks Ruthless.

I shake my head. What a miserable mess.

"What are you two going to do when I land a job and get my own apartment, hopefully not anywhere near all the grime and aimless wanderers? Are you going to call me all the time and ask me to bring over dinner or reset all the digital clocks?"

R & R look at me the way they would observe a stranger with mustard on his chin.

"Are you trying to make us feel helpless, Mr. Do-Goody, Mr. Chairman-of-the-Board?" says Ruthless.

"I think I've ruined my beads," says Reckless, analyzing one of them up close.

I feel like explaining the effect salt water has on things, but it's just too hot to bother. I will lie down on my back and try to put myself in a state somewhere between rest and sleep. I don't think it will take very long if these two keep quiet. Thankfully, they're not ones to gab very much, as surprising as it may seem. I take one last look out over the ocean and into the endless horizon and see a light pink developing. It will be another pitifully pleasant evening.

Deborah Fleming/Wind Horse

Do not bridle me today though the bright air beckons
and trees shine gold. So mild when you stroke me,
I am not the same when the west wind
bends the high grass in waves. Branches
flailing the air tell me lions crouch.

You have taught me submission
with your straw-filled stalls,
your barn bursting with hay,
the pasture that stretches, spring-fed
as far as I can see.

But on days of wind I know my own strength,
my size greater than boulders, my power
you cannot harness with your bits and straps.

The fierce howling that snaps tree limbs
wails to me of the predator's teeth.

Bridle me tomorrow
when the wind has gone into valleys,
when the storm has spun itself
into drops of dew.

Deborah Fleming/Hollow Road

Wind in high branches. Quarter moon
slices through clouds,
silvers the road.

Beyond a bluff and broken fence,
lights in farmhouse windows.
Above them in a break of cloud

stars rain down.
My horse leans on the bit,
steps off the gravel into the hollow,

stops, ears forward, raises his head; his barrel
tightens with a stifled sound.
The slopes before us rise,

waves that wash away stars.
Without a sign he gallops.
We swallow the dark hill.

Christine Hope Starr/What Made Me Knock?

It was a question about homework, was
the evening my period came, trouble
with the can opener. It was the dog vomiting
a bone, was a phone call, a form
that needed signature, a failure to follow
directions. It was running out of birdseed, was
wondering how long to practice ballet,
the smell of something burning. It was want
of her red gauchos, was a molar I lost,
a library book. It was my brothers fighting,
was a possum on the deck, bad weather on TV,
a squirrel drowning in the pool, was a door
left open, an ice cream truck, a friend spinning
cartwheels, a handsome spider.
It was my hamster packed with seeds.
It was their closed door, the quiet
behind it, and the worry when
I raised my fist, when my knuckles
brushed the face of it,
when Mom answered,
when I opened to her
shoulders sown with freckles
bare in bed and Dad
warbling nearby
and her eyes
bright,
glancing toward the bathroom, toward his song.

Christine Hope Starr/Berlin Subway

It isn't easy to rob me,
purse strap about my neck
twined
like a parcel
made to weather brute force.

But nobody is impervious—not even an American.

The pencil-thin wiener at the kiosk
lures my youngest,
so my purse falls
open,
and the leather wallet with a *zrrrt*

of the zipper, and the dark-eyed girl
at the kiosk sees everything: stitching
worn
along the edge of the zipper, each finger
paging unfamiliar bills.

Her breath quickens with the promise of all that cash.

She doesn't make shit
selling wieners
and stale Berlin pastries, so she decided
weeks ago she can live with being part of something
bigger, even if it is a ring of thieves.

The train is coming.

She hears the low drone,
knows how to time it,
hand off the wiener.
There is no time
to insert my wallet *and* close the purse.

Her dark eyes shut, her head bows the sign
to her accomplice, and somehow
it is satisfying
to go home at night
with that story just as they told her
it would be, after a long day underground—how

people with money are idiots, and why shouldn't she have
    nice shoes?

Karen R. Porter/Advice 5

In these
the strangest of days,
when dogs arrive at your door
and knock with their tails—
not looking for a handout
but just for some place
to hunker without shame,
and other creatures come—
wild and not so much—
wanting to talk,
to unburden themselves
of a million sundry horrors,
it is always good form
to open up, let them in.
If they knock, it is a mere request
entailing no concrete obligation.
Be polite to them.
They say the days
are breeding angels
in multiform abundance,
looking like devils
on the prowl.

Karen R. Porter/Told in Some Dark Wood

The evidence
spread before you:
a face in a cracked mirror,
a clump of soil and weeds,
four yellow hairs.

These
are the only things
you'll remember,
the only things
you'll need.

Your path
is not a long one,
but there are many twists and turns,
much scrambling
up and down.

If it rains
you might
wrench an ankle,
fall down in
astonishment.

Behold the soil:
dying weeds
holding fast
to a crumbling
foundation.

Behold the hairs
like strands of gold
or wheat
stroked thin by the
sun's hot hands.

Behold the face:
a line right
through the center
geometrically setting
everything askew.

Charles Rafferty/Watching Bumblebees in the South Jersey Pine Barrens

After walking fifteen miles into pitch pines,
I collapse in a clearing filled
with the oblong bells of blueberries
in flower. A half-dozen bees are mining them.
They never taste the same one twice
and they are methodical as they pull
the blossoms on like little bags. It is twilight.
The bees are fat and loud—louder,
at least, than the mourning dove
calling from a swamp that kisses the path
that carried me, louder than my blood
settling down after so many miles
of sugar sand, and louder than the F-16
dividing the sky with the chalk of its contrail
the way a teacher divides a blackboard
to begin a lesson. They seem almost frantic
as the sun dissolves behind a scrim
of needles and evening cloud—as if it had fallen
to these six bees to pollinate this patch
of horizoning berries. The fissure of honey
they have hidden in some log
must be draining into sand faster
than the blossoms can miracle out
of these twigs. It will be dark inside the hour—
the air black with the same night that hobbled
over Europe and the vast Atlantic.
The moon will not be up. I should be getting ready.

Mary Crow/Depression Perspective

It was that odd blurred waking when I saw
my arm sprawled on the edge of the bed
and startled—whose was it? A prickling,
ghost limb, but my arm lay there—I tried
to sit up, but my elbow buckled and I fell
back into that haze of who am I?

Now today will be empty with no poem to
prophesy another world where I can enter
these stories of depression that belong
to someone else, someone whose arm still
cradles her head filled with wobble.

That body stretched down my bed, flaccid
and pale, doesn't want to travel, doesn't care
to make itself into suppleness so it can
flex and float out to the river under my window.
Down there is someone's pubic hair, someone's
rounded belly and bony assemblage, the hum

of erotic arousal, and how can I stop it?
Look down: everything is disguised but it still
isn't mine: and the country inside is unexplored,
unknowable, stippled light under pines
from the shimmering moon, symbolic clothes
of some animal married to another animal.

Mary Crow/Air is the Heaviest Metal

A watery sound like a bamboo
Flute's, like the hum of planets:
        Blue: a drawn-out note
As I stare into the stranger's eyes,
        He who could only have come
From one direction—across the bridge.
        What can I promise him but chaos?
I was born in a howling star and my words
        Skitter over his skin with the keening
Of knives, like drops of dark sun.
        Want. Don't Want. Unfold.

Earth, air, fire, water: float in
        The repetitions of the room's dark:
Burnished as a dying star that pulls
        Everything into its swirling path,
He seems to be spinning me
        This way and that, furious and hungry,
We're a ripple in the space-time continuum,
        A mass of dense energy—
No light can escape our black hole
        Where galaxies erupt and burn.
We're sitting in this dark to listen to squeaks.
        Above, the skies turn shrill.

Brad Buchanan/The Nap Room

An old-fashioned room is best for naps
in the afternoon—the translucent drapes
domesticate and chasten the light;
the baroque wallpaper is exhausting to look at
and leaves the inside of your eyelids swirling
with trivial daydreams. The wooden ceiling
is a humble promise of man-made heaven—
democratic and vast, built with planks so even
and regular they could extend forever
and not be cramped. The mattress is lumpy
enough that you don't feel lazy. The empty,
elegant furniture has long attested
to the dignity of being well-rested
and the outdated art cries out for a little while
longer to come back, at last, into style.

Kenzie Gerr/Pop Goes My Mind

Who is he talking for?
The absorbent minds
Attached to the placid faces
A stifled yawn
A shift in posture
Ah that voice—
Beautifully monotones

Precious time hovering above our heads
Each bubble of a minute
Popped one by one
Useless facts and fluffed sentences
A picture of Aristotle in the class notes
(or was it Homer?)

Like watching a character on TV
Watching TV
Take me to the statues of Greece
Save me from this statue of a man
Sweet! I have killed a minute or 2
Wasted time captured with pen and paper
Proof I was here

An iPod earphone in one ear
Two glossed eyes on the teacher
3,4,5 other thoughts pop up
Then forced down by the heavy voice
Bye bye possible strokes of genius
Ah, yes, but back to the lecture

Judith Slater/Fortune

The fortune-tellers have taken over the town. I can't blame them. Who could expect them to resist the pull of the tides, the moon over the ocean, the roadside comfrey and wild thyme begging to be plucked and put into a tea to mend, or cause, a broken heart? No wonder we are on the psychic fair circuit.

This is the tail end of the season—the psychics most likely started in spring and worked their way north from Santa Monica. Still, it's a three-day Columbus Day weekend, and there's a respectable number of cars in the beach parking lot. A face painter must be part of the crew—the kids are walking around town with rainbows on their cheeks and butterflies on their foreheads.

It's a foggy morning, the kind that chills you all the way through. Which can't be good for the psychic fair, but I've lived here long enough now—six months—to be able to sense that this fog will burn off by noon. The sun will shine down and business will pick up. The fortune tellers probably already know that. Predicting the weather must be a cinch for them, one of the basic lessons they learn in tarot-card school.

I'm glad the fortune tellers will make enough money to pay for their groceries and their incense and the rent on their stalls, but I'm not tempted. I wouldn't mind having my face painted, but I don't want my fortune told.

I've begun to think about this a lot, and the way I figure it, we're allowed more than one life, and I'm not talking about reincarnation or the afterlife or anything complicated like that. I was a tomboy as a child, spent every spare minute climbing trees and catching frogs and lizards—that was one life. I was a hippie, or as much of one as you could be in Grand Island, Nebraska, in the seventies—that was one life. I was Jack's wife—that was one life, the big one. And now I have this new life, this ocean life, and it will be my last one. It will be my winding-down life, my peaceful life. I don't need a fortune teller messing that up, telling me things I don't want to hear.

The thing to do on a foggy morning like this is to walk downtown to West of the Moon and settle into one of its easy chairs and read a book and watch the fog float by the window in lazy curls.

"If only I had your hair," says Rebecca, West of the Moon's owner, the instant I walk in. She has a wind chime hung over the door, and whenever anyone enters or leaves, there's a nice fluttery chiming sound. "In this weather," she tells me, "my hair frizzes like—well, like a witch's. But yours gets those natural ringlets and I'm so jealous. Is that a new bracelet?"

Whenever I wear anything new in the way of jewelry, Rebecca's eyes seize on it. It's just costume jewelry, nothing special, I keep telling her that, but she doesn't care. It's the idea of something bright and sparkling that appeals to her, and I understand that. Rebecca and I sometimes run into each other at flea markets. We're kindred spirits. We'll buy a lone earring, its mate long lost. We think nothing of wearing mismatched earrings, or sometimes just the one all by itself.

"And you have no gray," Rebecca sighs. "That's the truth, isn't it? I can always tell if someone's dyeing." She pauses, gives me a stricken look. "Laurie. I'm sorry. Hair dyeing. You know what I mean."

"I know." But it's true—what she said gave me a chill just then. People tiptoe around me, with good reason. It's easy to say the wrong thing without realizing.

What I want to tell Rebecca is that a direct descendant of a bona fide Salem witch ought to be able to get her hair to do whatever she wants it to, but maybe if you're a witch, you have to pick your battles; you have to do trade-offs. Maybe Rebecca is allowed to have her smooth, unlined skin, or hair with no gray, but not both. And anyway, Rebecca is still an amateur witch. I think she got interested in genealogy the same way I got interested in dogs and gardening and the ocean, just for something to do, something to fill up the sudden emptiness. But once she discovered she was the descendant of a witch, her whole life shifted. A paradigm shift, to borrow that old hippie phrase. West of the Moon has become more New-Agey than ever since Rebecca became a witch, one entire wall devoted to books on magic spells and dream interpretation. And, sometimes, when she thinks no one's watching, I see her tracing the lines of her own palm. Practicing.

"I think your hair looks wonderful," I tell her, which is the truth. "Gray hair on someone as young-looking as you is glamorous. I wouldn't even think of dyeing my hair if I were you."

Rebecca could be a young sixty or an old thirty—maybe that's one of the characteristics of witches. In any case, she's gorgeous—even the teenage boys who wander in sneering and looking for trouble walk out besotted. Like a spell's been put on them, and maybe it has.

"You're a doll," says Rebecca. "That new gardening encyclopedia you ordered is in. Isn't this just the day for it? Curl up in that armchair and plan for a sunny day in June. What are you going to plant?"

I've been waiting for this gardening book. Once in a while I'll read one of Rebecca's books on dreams or spells, so as not to hurt her feelings. But she's willing to order the kind of books I like too. Gardening books, though she can't resist the ones with titles like *The Inner Gardener: Creating Your Own Sacred Spaces*. Dog books. Nonfiction books on nature, especially the ocean. You could read every book ever written on the subject of the ocean, and you wouldn't begin to know it all.

Thanks to Rebecca, though, I know more than I ever wanted to about other things. I know that if you dream about birds flying high, it means good luck, but if they are flying low, the luck you'll have will be bad. I know that magic spells to attract a lover are dangerous, and that in casting spells, it is far easier to attract a new lover than to convince a long-lost lover to return. This aspect of my new life here was not something I planned on. It just goes to show that even if you don't want to change, you change. Those little things, they'll get you every time.

This morning, I settle myself in the armchair at the back of the store. Not the one in the front window with the view of the ocean. I'm not greedy. I live by the ocean—I don't need to see it every minute of the day. (Even though I *am* making up for lost time, all those years spent in Grand Island, Nebraska, that island that was no island at all. Still, I leave the window chair for the tourists.) I open the encyclopedia, starting with R for roses, but then I put the book down. Because, all of a sudden, the rose garden I'm seeing in my mind's eye is not in my own back yard.

"What do you know about the Four Leaf Clover?" I ask Rebecca. She looks up from her knitting. Rebecca's the only person I've ever seen who can knit and read at the same time. She knits beautiful shawls out of the most delicate yarn. Rebecca makes knitting seem like a glamorous activity.

"It's for sale," she says.

"I know. I mean besides that."

"The usual story," says Rebecca. "It went broke. Winter doldrums. Tourists don't come here in the off season. Anyone who owns a motel here has to make all their money in the summer, or forget it. You should buy the place."

I'm pretty sure I never mentioned to Rebecca that I've been thinking of doing just that. Just trying out the idea, putting my toe in the water to see how it feels. What do I know about running a motel? Doing laundry? For other people? What am I thinking? Still, there's that "For Sale" sign I pass every day on my walks, and every day it seems to get shabbier, its letters so faded you can hardly read them.

I've been a tourist so often in my life, have been lost so often. Neither Jack nor I ever had a sense of direction. It was a failing in himself he hated, he who so liked to be in control. It would please me to greet tourists, to point them in the right direction, to steer them towards the new good struggling restaurant in town instead of the old, smug La Serre with the pretentious name and the mediocre food and the rude waiters, the ones who roll their eyes and shrug when you point out politely that there's no crab in the crab cioppino. La Serre keeps getting written up in the guidebooks and I just don't understand it except that the guidebook writers must be too lazy to come here and taste for themselves.

I would allow dogs at the Four Leaf Clover. I would make up gift packages for their arrival—dog biscuits, a towel to dry them off after a run on the beach, a generous supply of plastic bags, a big sturdy dish for their drinking water.

"You're dreaming, Laurie," says Rebecca. "I can see it in your eyes. You're creatively visualizing." Rebecca is big on creative visualization. This very minute she's reading a book on creative visualization while she knits a dusk-colored shawl.

"It's true, I am. I'm fantasizing. It's just an idea. Probably a dumb one."

"No no no." Rebecca puts down her knitting. "Your eyes are sparkling. And that's something I don't see very often, if you don't mind my saying."

"It's not that I need the income." I've never needed money, not since Jack. He had a gift for making money, freeing me to do, or not do, whatever I wanted. "But don't you think that a person who doesn't need money is in the best position to buy a failing motel? This way there's no desperation involved. I wouldn't be buying it and depending on it for my livelihood."

"Absolutely. I bought this bookstore on a whim. I walked by it and there was a for sale sign in the window and I knew it was foretold."

I'm not entirely sure I believe that last part. Rebecca is always saying things like this, ever since she discovered she's a witch, but she owned the bookstore before that.

I go back to my gardening encyclopedia, and creatively visualize a rose garden on the Four Leaf Clover's gone-to-weeds property.

Before long the air in the bookstore begins to smell like oranges. Rebecca is addicted to oranges, and she puts the peelings on the ancient radiator to perfume the shop. After a while the smell makes me hungry, and restless in a way I can't put my finger on. I can't even concentrate on a gardening book—my favorite kind of book.

I wander over to the front window. Three small girls, no more than eight, walk past, their faces painted with flowers. One's a rose, one a daisy, one a sunflower. They stop and use the bookstore's window for a mirror, giggling at their reflections, surprised at how beautiful they are. Then they race away. The psychic fair has stirred up all the atoms in this town. Watching the little girls run down the sidewalk, Rebecca gets a sad look in her eyes, and I wonder if she's wishing she had children of her own.

Rebecca has her own heartbreak—a broken engagement—but she doesn't talk about it much because I know she thinks her loss is trivial compared to mine. I don't see it that way. If I knew Jack was alive in the world, but not mine to have, I think it would kill me. I really do.

"Let's go have lunch," I say, though it's not all that far past eleven. The clam chowder at the Wheeler Café, the new struggling restaurant in town, will cure just about anything. Maybe even, on some days, a broken heart.

Rebecca hesitates for barely a second. "Why not?" she says. Since I am the only customer at the moment, it's easy for her to close up, to put her "Back in a While" sign on the door. It's not as though she'll lose important business. Any tourists still left in town will be at the psychic fair.

At the last minute she turns back and picks up her knitting bag, I don't know why. Surely even Rebecca, who can read and knit at the same time, won't be able to eat lunch and knit simultaneously. She slings the bag over her shoulder, tosses her silvery hair. She's wearing just one earring today, a moon-and-stars earring that jingles like a miniature wind chime when she walks. I'm wearing a lonely earring too, a teardrop pearl.

Outside, I see that I was wrong about the fog. It hasn't burned off, and it won't. It's settled in. So much for my powers of prediction. Well, a little fog never hurt anyone.

On the way to lunch, we pass by the Humane Society. It was a stroke of genius for the Humane Society to put its operation right on Main Street, in what used to be the old First National Bank Building. The Pet of the Week gets his or her own "Choose Me" cage in the big front window, and who can resist that? Thanks to the Humane Society, Wheeler Cove probably has the highest percentage of pet owners in the country, not to mention all the tourists who go home with an extra member of the family they hadn't counted on. But today there is no one in the "Choose Me" cage, and that's a relief. Pet of the Week has already been adopted, and it isn't even noon. My heart always sinks when there's someone in the "Choose Me" cage. I thought for sure by now I'd have a dog or two or three, a cat or two or three, but it would only mean something else to love and lose.

Lunch for Rebecca and me is always clam chowder. Sam the owner is a former New Yorker with ambivalent feelings—he claims to hate Manhattan, but he has Sabrett's hot dogs flown in every week. This is probably the only restaurant on the west coast, even including Los Angeles, where you can get a Sabrett's steamed just the way they do it at those sidewalk stands in New York. But I don't eat the hot dogs. I eat the clam chowder. Sam's clam chowder is like no other. No milk, no cream, pure essence of clam broth, a little potato and carrot and celery and parsley, fresh clams heated just till they curl, a spritz of lemon juice at the end. I like to think that if Jack had happened to come to Wheeler Cove on one of our vacations, I could have brought him here and had Sam set a bowl of clam chowder in front of him, and he would have been a happy man.

Sabrett Sam—we call him that, everyone does—used to flirt with me. He had me pegged completely wrong. He thought I was a transplanted New Yorker, for one thing, and when I told him nope, Grand Island, Nebraska, he laughed and didn't believe me. He wanted me to be what he wanted me to be. Now, no flirting. Obviously someone (Rebecca?) has sat him down and told him the score, because he won't even meet my eyes. He sets my bowl of clam chowder down in front of me with a respectful air, as though serving a meal-on-wheels to a shut-in. I get that a lot. People don't know how to behave around a newly widowed widow, and newly widowed widows don't know how to behave around people. Except for Rebecca. I sometimes know how to behave around Rebecca. Not always.

Not now, for instance. She's not eating her clam chowder, just looking down into the bowl the way you'd look into a crystal ball that held only bad news.

Rebecca and I take turns cheering each other up, though we never talk head-on about what's wrong. We talk *around* things, though, and sometimes that's almost as good. Today I think I know what's made her mood turn dark. She looks up and gives me a sad smile. When Rebecca really smiles, it just lights up your day. This is not that kind of smile.

"It's that 'Choose Me' cage," she says. "Every time I walk past it, I feel sad no matter what. I feel sad if the cat or the dog is still there, of course, because it means no one chose it. But I feel sad if the cage is empty, too. Because, someone chose *that* cat, but not another cat."

She's not talking about cats, of course. She's talking about Lloyd, who chose someone else. Who had the nerve to ask for his engagement ring back, probably so he could have the diamond reset into a new ring for the new fiancée.

To me, Lloyd looks just like his name—ordinary, even sort of lunkish. You'd think he'd be dazzled by Rebecca's beauty, that he'd realize he was the luckiest man in the world. It just goes to show you. . . something. Then again, Rebecca fell in love with him because he's a car mechanic, and that makes no sense either. Lloyd is one of those guys who can fix whatever's wrong, not just cars but plumbing and crossed wires and any inanimate thing that's broken. Rebecca told me he fixed her car in half an hour, after it had stalled out on cold mornings for years and no one else could figure out what was wrong. What Lloyd did was like magic, she said. But fixing cars is not the same thing as fixing loneliness, as Rebecca has discovered.

As if on cue, boring Lloyd himself, or maybe it's someone who looks very much like him, walks past the window of the Wheeler Café, his collar turned up against the chill. If it is Lloyd, this is not some huge coincidence. Wheeler Cove has a population of under four thousand, and there's no getting away from anyone. I hope Rebecca didn't notice, but of course she did.

"I have to leave," she says abruptly.

"You haven't even touched your lunch."

"Leave, as in move away." She's gone pale. "Would you rather buy a bookstore instead of a motel?"

"You can't leave." My heart is clenching up inside, in the way I thought it would never clench again. "You're my only friend."

"I'm not your only friend. Or if I am, it's only because you haven't made the slightest bit of effort. Plenty of people in this town would stand in line for the chance to be your friend."

"Plenty of men up and down this coast would stand in line for the chance to spend an evening with you. How can you let this one jerk who isn't good enough to walk into your bookstore ruin your life?"

Her eyes well up, and it makes me furious. Lloyd looks like his name, and acts like his name, and how on earth Rebecca could be pining away for him is beyond reason. But that's love for you—beyond reason. How is it that Jack and I found each other and knew right away, and never had even the slightest desire for anyone else? And how is it that someone like Lloyd could treat someone like Rebecca so cruelly and not feel the slightest remorse?

"I have to go," she says. "I don't have any choice anymore."

Everything is different for me, of course, but I do think I know how she feels. I haven't told this to Rebecca, to anyone, but one of the reasons why I moved to Wheeler Cove was because, back home, I kept seeing Jack's oncologist, and the night nurse with the mean raucous laugh, and the hospital chaplain who kept hovering with his "Stages of Grief" pamphlets even though we told him to go away. It wasn't really *them* I was seeing—it was people who looked like them. Everywhere, every corner I turned, every store I went into, waiting at every stop light. I thought the only way to escape them was to move away. And so far, it's worked. The wonderful truth is, I can't even quite remember what the oncologist looks like anymore.

I know it's wrong to blame those people. They were just doing their terrible job. Probably the mean nurse had no choice but to laugh, just to get through the night. And the chaplain—he probably thought he wouldn't be earning his salary if he didn't keep knocking on Jack's door like a vulture. But still.

That oncologist—he predicted the future as well as any fortune-teller. He told us three months, and he was right, almost to the day. Sometimes I think, did he have to be so stingy? If he had said four months, maybe Jack could have held on. We might have had that much more time together.

Afterward, I had to leave. There was no choice. So I understand.

I lean forward, pat Rebecca's hand. And then, because that seems like such a futile, empty gesture, no comfort at all, I squeeze the hand. I turn it over, palm up. She has the smooth, clean palm of a child, hardly any lines at all. To look at it, you wouldn't think she'd ever known real heartbreak. And maybe she hasn't, till now.

"If I tell you a secret," she says, "will you promise not to breathe a single word of it?" Rebecca leans forward, so that Sabrett Sam won't hear, but he's lost anyway in his Manhattan daydreams, leaning his elbows on the counter. Two fortune tellers are in the booth next to ours. One's eating a hamburger and the other a hot dog, which seems entirely the wrong diet for a fortune teller. But they have rings on every finger, and a musky incense smell swirls around them, so they must belong to the psychic fair. Maybe not fortune-tellers, but they're *something*—past life therapists, hypnotists, aura readers, chakra balancers.

"I tried spells," says Rebecca. "That's how desperate I've been." She runs a hand through her hair—not the hand I'm still holding—and the moon-and-stars earring jingles. The fortune-tellers cock their ears like dogs hearing a sound no one else can hear.

In West of the Moon, the Metaphysics section does not take itself seriously. The books have titles like *Better Dreams in 30 Days, Witches' Spell-A-Day Calendar, Chakras for Beginners*. Like the psychic fair itself, the tone is light, harmless, a pleasant diversion. Dabbling. That's how I've felt about Rebecca's recent interest in witchcraft, but it seems I've underestimated things.

"Spells to make someone love you," she's whispering. "Spells to make him turn against the woman he chose instead of you." She stops. Sabrett Sam is watching us, sensing something's up. I give him a stern look, and he turns away. "And the worst, the most desperate spell. The one to make him go away forever."

"Go away. . . how?" The steam from our clam chowder rises and curls in front of our faces like fog.

"The spell wasn't specific. Not exactly. Yes, it was. I had to take a bath at midnight, and light candles, and write 'Love me or die' seven times in brown ink, and other stuff I can't even bring myself to tell you." She's whispering faster and faster, and then she stops abruptly. She pulls her hand away.

"I hadn't seen him since that spell. I was beginning to think maybe it had worked. And the nightmares I had about that were worse than the nightmares I'd had before. And then today, just now, there he was." She gestures wildly at the window. "I knew the spell wouldn't work. I knew it wouldn't. I don't think I would have done it if I really thought it would work. But you do see what I mean, don't you? Staying here has made me crazy, and I don't have any choice any more except to leave."

"Rebecca—"

"No. No. I know you want to help me, but you can't. I shouldn't envy you, but I do. I know what you went through was so much worse, but your experience has more dignity, you know? You can't imagine how humiliated I feel."

She's right. I can't. She stands up, and before I realize what she's doing, she takes that twilight-colored shawl out of her knitting bag and tucks it around my shoulders. "It's yours," she says. "I was making it for you all along. I just finished it this morning while we were talking." And she rushes out before I can thank her or say anything at all.

I've always wanted one of Rebecca's shawls, but I've seen the hours and hours it takes for her to make one. I knew if I offered to buy one, she'd insist on giving it to me, and I didn't want her to feel obligated. Now that it's around my shoulders, it feels just like I thought it would, almost weightless, but warm. Just the thing for a foggy day. And I can't bear to think it's the only thing I'll have to remember her by.

"Was there something wrong with the lunch?" asks Sabrett Sam. The psychics stare at me curiously, picking up bad vibes, or purple auras, or an out-of-whack chakra. By the time I pay the bill and walk outside, Rebecca is nowhere to be seen, not that I could have seen her anyway in this thick fog. I walk back to West of the Moon, but the "Back in a While" sign is still on the door at the same crooked angle it was when we left for lunch. I hang around in front for a while, even though I know she's not coming back.

Next to a bowl of Sabrett Sam's clam chowder, the best cure for a broken heart I've found is a long walk on the beach. With Rebecca's shawl around my shoulders, I hardly even feel the cold. I could walk for hours, and I do. I pass some time throwing a stick of driftwood to a Golden Retriever, feeling half-relieved and half-regretful when its owner comes to claim it.

On the way home (is that where I'm going? I can't decide) I find myself on the old road that leads to the back of the Four Leaf Clover. Whoever owned the motel before had a green thumb, that's for sure. The paths are lined with baby's tears and ice plant, and each cottage has its own private garden of rhododendrons and hydrangeas, all neglected and wild now. The sea air is so hard on houses. Without someone to rescue these cottages they will rot from inside, and blackberry brambles and ivy will choke the gardens.

Creatively visualize, I tell myself. I shut my eyes, trying to see rose gardens in my mind, and the Four Leaf Clover sign newly painted, and dogs frolicking on the lawn, but what I see instead is Rebecca and that sad look in her eyes. And I think, there is something in us that can't help but reach out. Just when you've decided you can live a quiet life, a winding-down life, a closed-in-upon-yourself life made up of memories and the everyday grocery-buying present, it turns out you can't help looking ahead.

The living crowd out the dead. That's just the way it is, even though it's Jack's ghost I feel walking beside me on the grounds of the deserted Four Leaf Clover, his soft footprints I see in the sand. I circle the grounds of the motel, creatively visualizing, just getting used to the idea of this place being mine. And when I've come full circle, I find myself at the edge of the beach parking lot, where the psychic fair is just closing down. It's five o'clock, the end of a work day. The fog is so thick I can barely see the past-life therapists, the hypnotists, the channelers, the chakra readers, the dream interpreters, the face painter—all of them packing up, taking down their collapsible stalls, loading up their pickup trucks and vans. They look tired. It can't be an easy job, predicting people's futures, or their pasts for that matter. I wonder if the past-life people have philosophical debates with the fortune-tellers, or maybe they just have opposing softball teams.

The face painter's van is an old VW decorated with flowers. Once in a while I catch a whiff of incense. Or maybe it's pot; maybe that's how the fortune-tellers relax after a hard day. Mostly, though, all I smell is salt air and the ocean.

And then I smell oranges. I hear a sound like a far-off wind chime, and turn. Rebecca.

"They're packing up. They're leaving," she says. "I came down here so I could feel what it would be like to pack up and go with them, to never look back. It's the never-looking-back part that gets me."

"Me too," I tell her. "Also the looking-ahead part."

She looks miserable, and cold. She's not wearing one of her shawls, or a coat of any kind. I put my arm around her. The shawl she's made for me is like a magic shawl, made of yarn so flexible it expands and stretches to cover us both. Here we are at the edge of the world. The fortune-tellers have left us alone to fend for ourselves.

I open my palm, hold it out to her. I have an old woman's palm, but then I always have. Even as a child, so many lines.

"Go ahead," I tell her. "You can practice on me. Tell us our futures."

Douglas Collura/Away from Love

Away from love, I'm as calm as the dead.
Alone and calm. I didn't tell her that. You've
never been married, she asked, never? Didn't
chase it enough, I said. True, sort of. We
moaned our way across the sweating bridge.
She dove into sleep. I flopped in bed like
a dying fish. Into the daylight, I started
stopped started crying like hiccups. Her whole
startled face peered in. I didn't say, It's a prison,
being this close. Or, Someone held me under
scalding water when I was too young to escape.
How do you say those things to someone else?
On either side of the bridge, each body washes up
alone in its savage rendezvous. I'm calm again.

Douglas Collura/Great Knowing You

Somebody pushed, somebody pulled,
you arrived. For the record, Hello.
You grew, sort of. You were loved,
you were smacked. You were hugged,
you were strangled. Belts rotated
in the air like helicopter blades.
You cried before being hit. Good
strategy. In the dark, you saw a flying
Mr. Potato Head with claws. You still
see it. You grew, sort of. Anyway,
taller. You wallpapered a basement
room with *Playboy* foldouts. Drilled
spy holes from the back of your closet
into the bathroom. Somebody dropped
his whole giant body on top of you.
You survived but stayed suffocated.
Grew—working lazy, working hard—
sort of. There was nothing but you
and the world, crowded and empty.
The minutes disappearing. The future
never quite was. You stayed until
you left. For the record, Goodbye.

Laura Stott/Bone of My Hand

After I buried my hand in mud
I took irises home
and watched the wildness
fill my house
with violet.

Meanwhile my buried hand
held seeds in its palm.
I find a small white shell
—bring the shell to my ear,
but I don't

hear the ocean.
I don't hear the sound of
air hitting walls or beating of yellow wings.
I hear crows talk in their sleep.

They cover their black heads with blue wings
and say *Laura, build a flying machine.*
Grow at least one, or
if you like, plant the other
of your hands.
If you dare,
give up your legs, your waist, your whole self—

all but your eyes.
My eyes are like the sky, I say.
The black birds
flapping widely,
never timely.

Laura Stott/The Girl with No Hands

stole a silver pear
from his majesty's orchard.
And the gardener saw it, believed
she was an angel.
The way she tilted her head back
and stretched her neck to the sky,
to eat. Her hair hung like silk curtains.
And in the moonlight,
how could he not
fall in love with her?
How could he betray this love
and tell this secret
with the time to count each fruit?
Each destined
for their numbering.
It was a story the gardener couldn't
explain, but had to account for.
So, the gardener and the King waited
in hiding for the maiden
and when she appeared, hunger
was in the girl's every step.
They dared not speak,
but watched her, as moths lightly played
around their faces.
Are you of this world?
If I am a dream, then I am a dove.
Be my queen, I will make you hands,
and the gardener wept, and the king
kept what was never his to keep.

Kathryn Good-Schiff/In the Museum

Embryos in vials
washed of blood and stripped
of surrounding skin
show how waiting looks:
white dot,
squiggle,
bean sprout,
fiddlehead,
they curl as all things do when new.
What we were once, they will be forever.
This section of the exhibit sits apart
from the black lungs, enlarged hearts,
brains that died hemorrhaging.
Living bodies examine preserved ones:
the dancer shows every tendon, the cobbler every bone.
A canal-like corridor winds into
the womb room, darker than the main hall,
with a sign that cautions:
some may find the sight of a mother dead,
her baby still inside disturbing.
I see beauty.
I see where I came from, what I did at twenty-one.
The six-week fetus is the size of a fingernail.
It felt monstrous in my uterus
but now I can see it was only a beginning
with nowhere to go,
an acorn sprouted on a rock far from soil.

Kathryn Good-Schiff/Initiation

Advice for Persephone

Accept what is given:
hot chilies and rice on a steel plate in India,
mizuna leaves, salsa, tomatillos in Santa Fe.

The locals will smile and nod
if you eat with your hands.
You will feel alien only at the airport
where they suspect skin like yours.

Even in Hades
savor the six red seeds.
Every place you eat becomes home.

Susan Richardson/Thirteen Ways of Looking at a Penis

1

Molding the bushes of the estate
into elephants, apples, bears,
trimming this way and that,
the shear carves here a claw,
there a rabbit ear, all
from the inside out.

2

Grasping the
stick shift on a
sports car
cranking it
round and
round
wanting to
speed
stripping the
gears

3

so much potential
lies

in a white mush
room

propped upon a sturdy
stem

within the brown
woods

4

Curved shaft of a machete
sharp as a November wind
slicing open a virgin trail
vines wet with their own blood

5

Dog's tongue lolling out
dried chili pepper
hot day

6

Thick-trunked cactus
with an oval head,
its tip scorched by the sun
when a window
            intervened—

7

A man, a woman and a private coach
make three.
A man, a woman, a private coach
and a penis
make one.

8

Slim knife of a developer
sawing and hacking at hundred-year oaks
attempting the impenetrable wood

9

Flower bud, tiny, egg-shaped,
safekeeping, for a time,
its true, full-blossoming potential,
twin leaves curled up
tight as a baby's fist.

10

Erect missile, proud, tall,
offering to all a patriotic salute,
pointing the way to new frontiers,
Lewis and Clark in their slim canoe.

11

An imaginary yard
with real penises coiled in it!
Green, stiff, thin
conduits of nutriment,
wetting the parched-throat lawn.

12

Pushbutton-topped joystick
blasting every
virtually real invader—

13

After sex, a closed accordion,
soundless and purple
as a bruise

J.J. Penna/Money Years

I sit with my brother tonight at the Buddha Bar,
a love scene playing out with no sound
from an elevated screen above the table.
We're close enough to see how the closed captions,
sound of breathing and kisses,
make every tongue, every touch seem choreographed,
with body doubles working overtime on a California soundstage
for the perfect ass shot.

I'm writing down every word he says tonight
in case I lose him on one of his flights.
I remind him how desperately I once loved Eva Braun,
that promiscuous fugitive, some whirlgig of damage and regret,
alive and well on her first night in the city,
the kind of bombshell pilots painted on their cockpits
before long oceanic voyages.

How many nights we've sat here waiting to see
someone who might save us, like Sigmund Freud,
walking on the streets of the meat packing district,
calling us out to say WHAMMO, maybe the best thing
is to have no sensation.

We are animals, brother, meat steamers
in the steel pot of the city, too old to be renting.
Look at the men on the Henry Hudson tonight
driving into the tunnel.
Don't we have a couple of kids in Weehawken by now?
Aren't these the money years?
I'm starting to see signs all around us,
directions to the outer boroughs, notes for construction—
Sink Hole, Dig Safe.

Watch the vendors walk their meat carts
from Broadway towards some open lot near the waterfront.

I've seen their shiny metal crates sleeping under the open sky.
Some nights it's like the light comes down
for a moment, as if, at the end of every end of the world
there's a whole field of junk, a succession of chains
lit up by the lucky moon.

Zara Raab/Eclipse

At dawn, the house begins to stir.
Rising wind tugs strings of pollen
through the spring dark, and taps the bare
magnolia branches on the glass.
Someone's in the kitchen, humming,
scrubbing saucepans, sipping coffee.
A cup clatters in its saucer,
I slip out. Some days, I cut through
the manzanita woods; today
the street beckons, and I descend
into the crowd of cottages,
tarred roofs littered with pine needles,
the leaves of magnolia and oak.
I follow the tarmac seaming
the south side of town and stroll down
the sidewalk just as day begins—
by stands of sour lemonade,
past libraries of Poe and Proust
and the huts of furtive strangers,
past French and Japanese bistros,
gardens where marriages are made
under full moons, by vendors of
jewels, and haberdashers, past
the recording offices of
the constant egress of eclipse—
unnoticed, I stroll by them all,
the street a line on city maps,
source of woe and route of escape,
the sweet and sour rind of being.

David Gibbs/Approach

If I leave and you die   Father
     what then? Shouldn't I
     lead a meager life of slight survival
       and pumice my guilt
         smooth like slate?
                 My God
   my God I,   I
            my God—
who leaves who for punishment?

Can you see now? Here,
              let me drop this bottle.
    Look there,
its caramel cheek blushes shyly.
     Mother will be the one to clean it
                in the end.
       You were wrong not to discuss these things
          with me. Once   when convinced
            time clicked quick
               we shuffled our thoughts
        and had a good playing deck.
   We knew the cards, knew them well
       like pictures in a book of anatomy.

Maryfrances Gill/Vintage

Tiny chartreuse pearl
dangling from a dewdrop spangled scroll,
nestled on the smallest web-veined bed.
Receiving benediction from cloud, soil and sun,
unknowing the fate tomorrow brings.

Shall peasant foot crush out the blood,
whose sparkles seem to give another life?
Or shall the blood run bitter in its age?

Pearl, scroll and bed lie on a platter,
silver mirrored, fauns engraved surround.
Fine, long fingers, crimson nails,
take it to its final destiny.

Crystal Charee/Suspended

I'm working on a ten-year-old when the angel appears. The mother hovers anxiously, shadow playing dark halo to her baby's head. The angel kneels next to me, invading my personal space. "Adaeze."

"Not now," I mutter. The kid is unconscious.

"You can help her." The angel's voice echoes softly through my head, as my body is invaded by air fluttering from wings. It's like flying. I used to love that feeling. I resist.

"I am helping her," I say through gritted teeth. "Go away, Sera." I've never seen an arm this bad. It may have to come off.

The kid takes a deep breath and freezes. My heart stops until I realize that everything around me has become still. I look up and away from the terror frozen onto the mother's face. I abandon the kid, the mother, and the angel.

I resent sunsets. They remind me that everything beautiful is fleeting. With time suspended, the sky melts in layers of eye-burning pinks and oranges. The psychedelic sky has converted distant mountains of dull brown to purple and blue.

A mutilated car door is the only obstacle between the edge of the bridge and me. The railing is smooth and wet looking. I rest my forearms against the cool, painted metal and wish for a crack or a nick that I could chip away at.

The bottle of oregano oil that I keep stashed in my pocket is something I pull out more from habit than need. Harsh pepper sears the underside of my tongue and then climbs up my nose, smelling like Christmas. It overrides the melted metal and burnt glass of the accident and overpowers the flavor of stopped time, which mingles in the passageway between the nose and tongue like grace-flavored lollipops.

The angel steps up to the rail beside me. I feel like I'm wading through dunes of baby powder, lifting my head to catch fat, white snowflakes on my tongue. The snow tastes like cinnamon and is warm and soft as a sun-kissed rose petal. I want to surrender, to do anything the angel asks.

I started seeing Sera when my brother was born. This was back before I knew that only crazies and charlatans talk to angels. Enda had a lot of health problems when he was a baby. It was part of God conditioning us,

warning us not to get too comfortable having Enda in our lives.
I hate the angel. I feel disloyal.

"Why now?" I want to know. "You've been bugging me to heal people for years. What is so important about this girl?" I turn and stare over at the girl. She looks like Manny's kid. Older, but with the same dark hair and sweet spirit.

"We're just friends," I mumble.

If I look for him, I'll probably find him helping a bloody octogenarian. I gravitate toward kids. I figure the old ones are already on their way out, so if they go out less a limb or two, at least they had a whole body for *most* of their lives. . .

"You kissed him," Sera says.

I rub the gooseflesh on my arm, raised by her palpable amusement. "No I—" But I did. I remember. I hadn't even been drunk.

Manny had been leaning against the van after work, waiting to drive me home. He was flipping through his pack of baseball cards. He has some good ones. When he paused, I knew he wasn't looking at a card, but a photo of his daughter that he keeps stashed in the pack.

"Hey," I said when I reached him. "Take me to McDonald's."

Manny sighed. "No."

I grinned. "Yes."

Manny's too nice. He hates taking me there because I like to pick at a salad and make fun of fat people. The restaurant is only a block from work. We sat on stools, at a fake bar set-up, with a view of people ordering. "Look at that one," I said. "If she ever needed to haul ass, she'd have to take two trips." I nibbled at a dry square of iceberg lettuce. Bunnicula must have gotten to the tiny carrots before I did—they were mostly white.

Manny shot me a mock glare. "I hope my mama doesn't walk through that door. . ."

I couldn't help myself. "Why? Does she make Jabba the Hutt look anorexic?"

"You are never, ever meeting her." He laughed and then changed the subject. "Espy just got braces. Her teeth hurt."

My cheeks were hot. I'd be nice to his mother. I reached out my hand, and he handed me his pack of cards. I found Esperanza between Carlos Peña and B.J. Upton. Six years old in the photo, with missing teeth and long dark braids. It's a school picture that was taken four years ago. Before he and Jasmine were divorced. It's the last picture of Espy, he always says, without resentment in her eyes.

I tried to picture braces over the gap in her teeth. "Did you spring for the invisible ones?"

"Yeah. You don't really notice them too much. But she says they hurt. She has a boyfriend too." He sounded a little lost.

Manny had an elbow propped on the bar top, resting his head on his hand. I was facing the counter, but he was facing me. He had one foot hooked onto the rung of my stool, arm draped over his thigh. When I turned to say something comforting, I felt encircled by his long limbs.

"I think I'll get some ice cream," I said, shooting a glare at my salad. There was no line at the counter, but I didn't want to move. Manny radiated heat and safety. I handed Esperanza back to her father. His hand closed around mine. I tried not to look at him, fighting the wave of attraction that was rare and unwelcome.

I thought I had it covered, but I glanced up too soon. Manny was looking into me, smiling. He saw me, and he didn't run screaming away. One hip, one shoulder, one cheek tingled with heat. The other half of my body wanted to. I kissed him.

That essence of Manny, the joy of being near him, intensified. His love would never melt or fade away like ice cream or sunsets.

"Stop it!" I step away from Sera. "I didn't feel all that," I say. "You're embellishing." She steps toward me, her face gentle. "You've been repressing how you feel about him." Her voice hardens. "I don't lie. You know better."

I fight off a flood of remorse and shame. I look away. "Whatever."

When I was nine and Enda five, he received a lifelong ban at my friend Joan's house after his first visit to their garage. Joan's parents, and mine, tried to explain to him why it was a bad thing to let all of the snakes and rabbits out of their cages.

Enda heard none of it. He stood with legs planted, hands on hips: Peter Pan facing down an army of Captain Hooks. "How dare you," he said, cutting at Joan's parents with indignant eyes. "How dare you put those animals in cages?" He spread his arms and threw back his head. "They need to be free!"

By thirteen, Enda had modified the treehouse and the garden shed, turning them into animal hospitals. For his trouble, he received countless bruises, bee stings, and a variety of animal scratches. Sera would help me heal Enda from whatever his patients inflicted on him throughout the week.

Enda was trying to coax a stray cat out of the neighbor's tree. I sighed. "Come on. You can get the cat later." The locker next to mine belonged to a cute guy whose name I didn't know yet. Even though I hung around my locker after every single class, and before and after school, the only time I saw him was first thing in the morning. I hadn't gotten the nerve to mumble anything other than *good morning* yet, but I was working on some interesting things to say. *Hi, I'm Adaeze*, was as far as I'd gotten but I was convinced that, as an opening line, it was too cliché.

"I'll catch up," Enda called down. "I almost have her."

I hesitated. Mom was paranoid about us walking together—me, because I was a girl, and Enda because he was a flake. He was thirteen. He could make it to school on his own for once. "Just leave her. You're going to be late."

"Go," he said. His voice was calm for the cat with a hint of impatience toward me.

"Fine," I said, and went. I was almost an adult. I didn't have to keep chasing after some little kid.

I don't know how long he was up in that tree before the cat took a swipe at him, and he fell out of the tree, but Mom was pissed when I got home. He had scratches on his arm from the cat and a sprained ankle from the fall.

After Enda fell from the tree, Sera came. "We're not to do the healing this week."

"See? This is what you get," I told Enda. "You're too reckless." I was still smarting from the two-week grounding I'd gotten. I couldn't believe how paranoid my parents were. Enda wasn't going to *die* because I didn't walk him to school.

"What?" His eyes moved back and forth from me, to where Sera stood. He couldn't see her but he could see where I was looking. Sometimes, I'd test him and stare at a place she wasn't standing. He always went for it.

"We're not healing you this week."

"Really?" He looked confused and sad. "I feel kind of sick."

He had been quiet since the tree incident. I figured his ankle was bothering him. "Why can't we heal him," I asked Sera. "Is it because he did this to himself? Because he got me grounded?" This last bit was said with a tinge of hopefulness. It would be nice if God were on my side. My parents weren't.

Sera's eyes were sad. She shook her head. "This isn't punishment."

I felt bad. "Can't you even heal his sprain?" I didn't want to have to be his nurse and waitress all week.

She hesitated. "I can heal his ankle," she said.

The way she looked at me made me uneasy, but I shrugged. "Okay." How bad could cat scratches get? There wasn't anything else wrong with him. . .

She healed his ankle but she wasn't there when he started to get paranoid and hallucinate. She wasn't there when he was misdiagnosed. She wasn't there when my brother died. I'll never forgive her for that.

"I was there." Sera says it with such conviction that I search my memory, looking for her. Nothing. A black hole, angel-less, Godless. Her eyes swim with promises she couldn't make.

Spit bubbled at the corners of Enda's mouth. Circles under his eyes made his cheeks sag. He looked a million years old. I leaned toward Sera over my brother's hospital bed. A sadness that emptied me of hope spilled out of her eyes. "I need you to help me," I said. "Help *him*."

"It's his time," Sera said, and I remembered all of the times I'd heard her say that. All of the times she'd had me heal people, and all of the times she'd stopped me. I'd been able to accept it when those people belonged to someone else. Her sorrow had always been a balm for my helplessness. Now it made me angry.

"He's thirteen. . ." I looked at him. His face was flushed, but his eyes were shining; they were focused on the angel.

"I can see her," he said. "Hi, Sera."

She smiled down at him. "Hello, beloved."

He reached out to touch her face. Another presence made itself known. A light spread throughout the room, brighter than my eyes could take in. I closed them, but the intensity shone through. The corners of my heart gladdened, despite my despair. The light didn't dim, so much as become invisible to my eyes. Here was the originator of the love that flowed between my brother and me.

"God," I whispered.

He reached out His hand to me. Although I was several feet from Him, I felt the caress—the stroke of my hair, compassion that soothed the worries from my mind.

Enda stood on the bed, a warm glow seeping through his skin. Joy and peace softened his features, taking age, leaving wisdom. He leapt for God, who caught him with a laugh that was deeper than my ears could hear. It shook me to the bone. Enda wrapped his arms around God's neck, laughing too.

Then there were two Endas. One lay on the bed, eyes closed—an ugly, empty shell. I turned my gaze to the other Enda. He was all glow. Just beauty, no skin.

Bitter sorrow slashes my throat. Comfort softens the air, wrapping itself around me. I try to fight it, like I have for years, but I'm too weak. I inhale the proffered peace, through my skin, into my soul.

I move away from Sera's embrace, parting the wings she wrapped around me. The girl sleeps. I can't look at the mother; I know too well how she feels. My bag lies open, forsaken. I crouch next to it but I don't look inside. The tools in it are useless. God—

"What do you need me for." I hear no inflection in my voice; feel no movement of my soul within my body.

Sera stands next to the mother. They look down on me. The mother is a pillar of petrified distress. Sera's face is compellingly peaceful. "Wouldn't you like to be a part of her healing?"

"Ten years old, only ten years old," her mother had repeated as a mantra over my head, only a few moments ago. The girl is tan with lots of long dark hair spread around her head. Her lips curve up at the corners. I wonder what kind of dream God is giving her right now.

I'm suddenly thankful for the fossil who probably has Manny's attention fixed. I know the toll a loss of a stranger takes on him. He feels responsible, as if he should have done more, been more. This girl could be Esmeralda. *Prevent that heart attack, Manny. Don't look over here.* I try hard not to care. I don't want him to see me say no.

I take out the bottle of oil again, then roll it around in my hands. The oil is Manny's habit. I adopted it because it distracts me from the bleeding, the writhing, the death that I see every day. It helps me ignore Sera, standing over my shoulder, nudging me. I set the bottle aside.

The girl starts breathing again, and the world gets loud. "Wait, wait! I haven't decided yet!"

The girl's mother stares down at me. "Decided what?"

Panic roars through my blood. I hear it screaming through my eardrums. I want to run, but I close my eyes instead. "Please, God," I whisper. Anger at God and pity for the girl war within the pounding of my heart; the clench is rage, the release, mercy. "Please, God." A familiar focus breaks through sound of thrumming blood, smoothing out my heartbeats until betrayal and forgiveness are almost one.

The girl's arm is black, wrinkled, bloody. Bones poke through flesh with no regard for grace or humanity. I stroke the length of mangled flesh and bone. A kiss from God flows from the top of my head to the tips of my fingers.

Compassion for the girl overwhelms me. The person who refused to help her seems so far from who I am. Love flows freely through my veins, drowning self-disgust.

The girl's eyes are still closed. I stroke her brow and catch the tail end of her dream. *The heat of the sun shines through the curtain of water, warming us, though the spray is cool. We dive through the fall of water, into the sea below. Dolphins with tattoos made of dancing rainbows, welcome us with shrieks of laughter.*

The girl stirs, bringing her healed arm up to touch the space between her eyes. "Mom?" She rises a little, resting on her elbows.

"I'm here." The woman is in Mom Mode. She keeps her voice calm and authoritative, even when she asks, "Can I hold her?"

"Yeah, go ahead." I'm surprised. Most civilians don't ask. Parents are often the biggest obstacle to overcome when I try to help a kid.

The girl looks at me over her mother's shoulder. She is bemused, but there are worlds of personality in her eyes. I look at her, and I know why Manny includes that particular photo with his baseball cards. Pictures, especially posed ones, rarely capture a person's true essence. I stand.

Her eyes follow me. "Are you Adaeze?"

"Espy! I saw the car—Espy, are you all right, baby?" Manny approaches. Adrenaline makes his long-limbed gait unusually graceful.

Esperanza's mother is helping her to stand. "Pops! I'm okay." This last part is muffled by a mouthful of her father's shoulder.

"You're okay?" His voice goes from panicked to relieved. "You're okay, you're okay. . ."

He spots me. I can see all of the times he's teased me for helping children first, play across his memory. He smiles.

I smile, too, but he pulls his focus back to his daughter. He gives Jasmine a hug. She's short and a little chunky. I remember all of the fat jokes I've made that he's never laughed at.

The fresh breeze of time suspended has blown away on the wind. The reek of burnt glass climbs up my throat. Blood and fear make the air sting with desperation. Bodies, some attended, some abandoned, litter the road. When I first started as an EMT, I would scan an accident, looking for someone I knew. I do that now. Dread runs along the inside of my skin, searching for a way to burst out.

"Adaeze."

"What?" I turn away from Sera, hoping, though I know better, that she takes the waver in my voice as anger rather than terror. I imagine flipping through Manny's pack, each card depicting a ten-year-old girl with braces and one arm. Fiery shame inches up my arms and settles like a nettle necklace around my throat.

Sera stands beside me and brushes a hand over my hair, following my ponytail to the tip. She tugs gently, tickling my skull.

"Forgive yourself," she says.

Mark Burke/The Two Lobes

Before we began to write,
when breathing was still a blessing
exchanged between the soul
and the spirit of the world,
when a jealous god had not yet
forbidden the many, the two lobes
ran separate, two voices sounding
in our heads, one about goats
and the claims of winter, the other about
righteousness, a voice that rained
when death stained the air.

But the codes scratched in stone,
the ash inks scrolling across
dried lamb skin, began to stitch one
with the other, drawing the lips together,
closing the fissure so only one god
would fit, claiming the territory,
banishing the confiscated spirits,
dragging his cape to brush the tracks flat.
Oh, to be the soul who hears
the sky sing in the wind, these voices
breathing when the sewing comes
undone, the stories from the fires
spilling behind our eyes.

Mark Burke/The Girls

The noisy ones call from the top canes,
candy lips spilling invitations
across the evening air like girls
teasing from an upstairs window
daring you to kiss.

Not so high on the shoots,
other jewels to greet your eyes,
flames shining along a green shore,
sirens lighting the way with their torches,
still tart, not yet grown.

But the older ones hiding under
the skirts of leaves, these raspberries
are the sweetest, their reds have turned
a deep maroon in the slow alchemy
of light and water, heating your skin

when you touch them to your mouth,
that way she warmed you in the dark,
standing between the parked cars
after the dance, opening her blouse,
brushing her breasts to your lips.

Tera Vale Ragan/Bullet 33

Virginia Tech, April 16, 2007

As blind as a mole's
head in
     soft moss stones
i had been in the deep

     left pocket
of his tan vest.

i didn't know the
purpose.
i heard the others
          fired
and did not think
     it odd,
so accustomed as they were
to paper
     hits
at a practice range.

The first
two-of-ten-per-magazine
had felt the warm sheets
         bleeding
in the West Ambler dorm.

The others, just as foreign
as the language
in each classroom:
     trente,
         dreißig,
            thirty,
left the searing black barrel
of the Walther P22
and needed no
     translation.

The trigger
          popped,
breath
        skipped
                  breath,
a girl leaped
            from a granite sill.

i didn't know how
long,
if only for a
        second
i had
        hit
the darkness
        of his twisted
    cerebrum

or if the sparrows had
                merely silenced
                        the sun.

*Marilyn Joy/*Who's in Control?

That quick it's
all ash, all
in someone else's living room
or basement, or on the back
of a truck.

Dragged out to sea
with a wall of water,
lost in a bad business deal, a
card game, a
plummeting market.

And you were so careful
to put out the candles, lock
the doors and windows,
listen to the weather report,
calculate
profit and loss.

But it fell apart anyway, failed,
fastened itself to an anchor
and sat on the bottom
of an indifferent sea.

Is it the illusion of control
that keeps us going? Muttering
inside our mind about
next time and
if only they hadn't,
or I had.

Maybe the truth
of one's failure with dominion
would cause mutiny on

this oily sea of life—
leaving God to deal with
these floundering, cranky souls.

Better to let us
think we're in charge, enjoy
a little heavenly peace
in the interim,
and break it to us gently, on our
way out of town.

Mark Wisniewski/Community

I didn't know they would steal
from your desk
on the legal assumption that they
owned your desk & office
& were thus
entitled

they did this
to me more than once
but the first few times
I thought I'd misplaced
whichever document
their rules required me
to have kept

so even I believed in their
accusations regarding my
disorganization

but the day I needed the letter—signed by
my boss—
proving he'd promoted me for
"remarkable excellence"
I knew they had stolen it
because I'd taken
pains to file it in a clearly
marked folder
& now that folder was
empty

I needed that letter to prevent them
from firing me for having lost

the other documents they'd taken &

their lawyer then
informed me that if I accused

them of having stolen
anything
they could terminate me for lack
of collegiality

so I didn't
accuse anyone

until I hired
my own lawyer

who then accused
everyone

causing my boss to send me
a memo stating I'd missed
his deadline for filing responses to
termination letters

of course I had never
received
a termination letter

& when I
finally did

it was
dated 3 months
earlier—

all of this proving that
when it comes to teaching literature
on the community
college level

I have
failed

Mark Wisniewski/As with Love

the ice on the lake
disappeared in one day

this began
where the creek flows in

Centa Theresa/To My Daemon

When we meet,
in a world undivided
by night or day,
I'll gather myself to you.

Nights I lay sleepless,
thoughts churn until they hum
through me, filling dreams
with your praises.

When you are close enough
to touch I will study your stillness,
and how you sleep, in wonder
of such exquisite singing.

Until then I'll inscribe the tawny
page, the autumn branch,
wishing you were as real
as these two ochre-eyed cats
who lie purring by my thigh,
the nameless one who sneezes,
and the one with a name.

To meet you first hand,
tracing my longest breath,
I'll catalogue every key
in this house, then take to the open,
pedaling my bike,
its single beacon fanned
across the coal blue night.

Riding your scent, I'll double
as the crescent moon lighting
dark pastures, streaming through
thickets of forgotten dream.

On the roadside to nowhere
I can imagine, I might find you
basking in a pool of mud and stars,
under the clear night sky.

Immersing my body
in the dark-jeweled loam,
I'd extend my hand,
and having found you, at last,
abandon this divided world.

Centa Theresa/**Mendocino Headlands**

Spring at the headlands: ambling through
fields of yellow broccoli, dusty, purple cabbage,
pale radish stalk, to the cliffs' edge where, below us,
redwood stumps drift in and out with the tide.

The walk down to the rocky shore, parched
grin of a bone we thought might be whale,
seals at the mouth of the Navarro.

I want always to remember the single glass
in the windowsill, and you reminding me,
in countless ways, how we are meant to be
in surprise—like the sheet rolled back to reveal

two missing blue socks—we aren't to know
a thing before it arrives, so the foothold
can enter us unnamed, our selves
being the clay this world hollows out.

Octavio Quintanilla/Welfare

As long as our stoves fatten with heat,
we bring order to our tables.
We declare to the universe:

We are masters here.

Today, winter is the old beggar
we welcome into our homes.
We let him have it all,
even the blanket we fight over
when days resemble the ribcage

some animal's flesh abandoned
by the side of the road.
One of us points to the remains.
They become symbol and fable:
Once we ate the dirt moistened by rain.
Once we fed each other sleep.

Now we are going somewhere.
Let us rejoice, then, and remember the days
when the tongue was the only meat
we could bite into.

Octavio Quintanilla/Sonnet with All Its Grief Cut Out

The mailbox of your life, always empty.
The woman you loved twenty years ago
Sleeps and breathes next to her plumber husband.
      Their kids, all grown up. The house is quiet,
Ready once again to be filled with moans.

      You lie listening, your eyes closed, awake
Sucking on the nipples of the huge night.

Justin Polikaitis/Beauty

It is lonely being free, when those around you
Make no effort to break bonds.
Like caged birds without burden,
They cannot see beyond the bars' bounds.

Not knowing who to blame for absurdity,
We bark at the benevolent and brew malcontent.
A bluntly bleak outlook, a skewed view,
We balk happiness, begetting sorrow.

Like a baleful barometer we embrace our bane,
Betray our ideals with morose laughter,
Bequeath our dignity through bedlam,
Bereft of pride. Our virtue burnt away.

We turn a blind eye, afraid to discover
We have become what we abhor.
Abandoned by even that part of us
That braved the dark for so long.

We are reduced to banality, a beast in an abattoir
Sent on an oblique path, shambling into obfuscation;
Standing balanced on the brink, hypnotically staring
Down black maw's oblivion. Beaten and broken.

Only to be taken aback, to observe a single spark
As bright light. A boon belated to the eleventh hour.
Once abstract, now obvious. Buried, now bare
In all directions, blessed epiphany from nature.

One truth exists
To make us take
That next breath;
Fight on in battle.

Jean Howard/Epitaph of James Minakakis

"From Darkness he came,
In Darkness he lived.
To Darkness he returned;
And from Darkness he will be
reborn to a better time. 1952"

James Minakakis,
upon your tomb
the sky falls back
onto great trees the color
of death itself.
In this black mirror
life wears silver,
drinks up light.
An ant scrambles, its
universe granite.

Mr. Minakakis,
dogwood leaves cast
their souls,
dry negatives upon
your surface.
You light a dark fire
in my mouth
as I crawl
upon your shoulders,
spread my arms,
touch calves into dust.

Let granite the color
of every nightmare
braid my hair,
coil it under
like a surgery of stone.

My elbows punctuate
its surface.

By pressing pelvis
to your corners,
Mr. Minakakis,
I feel it begin,
words on silence,
the come-shutter
of the living.

Pierre Hauser/Learning from Los Angeles

She'd given me one last chance and I'd blown it. But I was still there, under the same roof. It was a childcare issue. If my wife kicked me out, she'd have to pay for a babysitter. It was a lot cheaper to have me around "scratching my nads," as she put it—or, as I liked to see it, serving as an inspired teacher and playmaster for our two boys.

My crimes were the usual ones: I couldn't resist certain complicated women. (The blown last chance: my wife caught me naked, reading Shakespeare, to a plump redhead.) Plus, I hadn't worked in several years. Suitable openings didn't crop up that often for someone with my knowledge base (MA in sociology, PhD in history, almost). I'd once been an assistant professor at the community college level. I'd conceived some novel business ideas that hadn't yet born fruit.

We were living in Los Angeles that summer, off Wilshire, near the tar pits. In June, Jody's paper supply company had dispatched her from Dayton to whip the LA office into shape. They'd found us housing in a condo complex left half-finished when the developers lost their financing. The design featured fanciful details meant to suggest a French chateau, but the primary sensation was entropy, the way a crenellated plaster wall would dissolve into a lattice of metal rods or a tree-lined stone path would terminate in an arid swath of nettles.

In a way, I'd bottomed out, living in that aborted development, barely speaking to Jody. But I felt strangely hopeful. It was so gorgeous outside, all that lemon-scented foliage and well-groomed humanity. Each day I woke up on the couch and there were flashes of brilliant light leaking under the blinds, as though someone was out there photocopying.

One morning, I was in the hallway grabbing the paper when a pack of four kids bounded by, headed toward the apartment at the end, siblings I guessed from their staggered ages. My eyes fixed on the girl in the rear, a Botticellian beauty with strawberry blond ringlets, light blue eyes, freckles, about 20 years old.

"I can't believe it. It's like the first good thing that's happened to me in so long," she burbled, and her three brothers smiled supportively. Below her smile, I noticed as she passed, something quivered, ready to give way— her eyes looked accustomed to crying. She wore heavy black boots, jean cut-offs, knit gloves with the fingers cut out. After the boys disappeared into their home, she wheeled around, pointed her finger at me, made a firing motion, and blew on her fingertip.

"Looking for a statutory rape charge to add to your accomplishments," Jody said, standing in the open doorway, wolfing down a banana.

"She's not that young," I said. "You look nice today." Jody was wearing a clingy skirt that nicely outlined her backside. She rooted through piles of clothing on the bench, which meant she'd lost her keys, which I quickly located next to the coffee pot without receiving a thank you. While she scanned the paper, I massaged her shoulders, which she pretended not to notice. On the way out she said, "Try not to spend the whole day inside watching TV."

As if I would move to the nation's second biggest city and not want to thoroughly explore it! I'd perused the literature and so was aware, for example, of LA's importance as the template for the sprawling decentralized mode of urbanism that subsequently proliferated across the Sun Belt. I went to wrangle the boys into clothes and found Teddy, our sweet six-year-old, putting on his mother's bra again, which I refused to be concerned about, in spite of his long lashes and girly hand gestures, because the preeminent parenting manuals described it as normal. I located ten-year-old Jack throwing pop flies in the living room, frowning at a CNN report on corruption in Russia, the budding athlete and precocious student of human frailty.

When we opened the front door to leave, the change in air pressure stirred up the odd smell that emanated from the vicinity of the kitchen cabinets, the sharp tang of dusty cement mixed with dirty river, plus hints of coconut and citrus. Back on our first day, I'd thought the smell came from whatever amalgam of wood byproducts had been fused to form the cabinetry, but after removing a garbage bag that patched a hole inside a cabinet, I discovered the smell came from inside the walls. Along with the earthy odor, there was also the sound of trickling water, sensory reminders that however much man remade the California landscape, the real environment was still down there, living and breathing.

We headed off to our first destination of the day: La Brea Tar Pits. They were only three blocks away—it seemed crazy we hadn't seem them yet. We strolled the sloping lawn past several ponds inhabited by plastic wooly mammoths.

"What's so great about these pits?" Teddy asked finally. "It looks like water." He was right—whatever tar was present had sunk beneath the surface, leaving only a trace of multi-hued slickness.

"This is the pits," I said and they roared with the comic generosity of the young.

Our next stop was Petersen's LA Automotive Museum, whose parking lot, appropriately enough, was bigger than the gallery space. I was disappointed the museum provided little historical context, failing, for example, to note the car's key role in the decline of downtown. But it did boast the original Love Bug, rare Hot Wheels, and a sizeable hands-on section. Teddy found a Laura Ashley print in the dress-up chest and wore it while pretend-cruising in a Model T with his pretend-husband, Jack, who was sporting goggles, a cap, and a scarf.

I gravitated toward a '72 Ford Galaxy that had been covered with chalkboard material on which children were encouraged to draw. As I doodled on the hood, I had an inspiration: why not put out a line of actual vehicles with this exterior? Imagine every day you could draw yourself a new car. Going shopping? Write your grocery list on the door. I jotted some notes in my journal, considered who'd be appropriate backers.

"I'm going to have to ask you to leave," said a guard with a lip ring and blue hair.

"What?" I looked over at the boys, wondered if they'd broken something, like the time at MOCA when Teddy tenderly hugged a Calder and the whole thing toppled.

"Profanity is not something we can allow in our interactives," he said. Do you allow it elsewhere, I wondered. He pointed to the chalkboard car on which I'd written several times, "Jody Cutter is a fatuous fuckwad."

"Words, words, words," I said Hamletically.

"We haven't reached South America yet," Teddy wailed when I said we had to go.

"Dad got into trouble," said Jack, attuned to the hard truth of things. As we boarded the elevator, the Botticellian girl and her youngest brother materialized. She was running her fingers across the boy's buzz cut, evincing a tactile impulse I shared.

"Someone got busted," she said. "Fight the power." She raised a fist ironically.

"This guy apparently believes in freedom of body disfigurement but not freedom of speech," I said. We spilled into the entryway, and Teddy got the brother playing tag.

"My name is Tiffany, by the way. Do you love this place? Righteous gift shop. Looks like we're both on nanny duty. Oh, this is Jamie, who's seven. Whoops, no, eight." She unselfconsciously adjusted a bra strap.

"I'm Ray. How extraordinary to encounter each other twice in one day."

"We should double-date some time. I mean you know, give the boys a play date."

Her struggle for words suggested an overabundance of thoughts colliding and caroming. She had a bubbly energy but seemed conflicted about letting it flow.

"I was supposed to go to college back in Tulsa, but Dad got a new job in LA and now I have to be the nanny for a year because he doesn't trust people here or something."

"I'm sorry. And your mom?"

"She died when I was little. So, listen, we're having a kind of party on Friday night. Dad's going to be working late and some of our crew are coming by."

"Well. . ." My spirits soared, imagining the freewheeling exchange of ideas good parties can bring, but I hesitated to say "yes" without knowing my domestic schedule.

"Oh there will be some people who are old," she said, misreading my hesitation.

"Who are older, I mean. My older brother has varied friends. What are you, like 34?"

"Thereabouts." She was short by seven years—not enough to quibble.

Shifting weight from foot to foot, noticing an ink spot on her left forearm and trying to rub it off with spit, redoing her ponytail, redoing it again, she put me in mind of Cherie, the plump redhead in Dayton, all that vibrating energy. But with Cherie what drew you in was a surfeit of sexual desire that seemed remarkable for a 45-year-old wife and mother, whereas with this girl it was a wounded but indefatigable spirit I was determined to learn more about.

Unfortunately, Jody had a meeting the night of the party, so I had to stay in. But the boys helped me make the best of it. The white walls became a green screen for our masculine imaginations and the $2.99 bouncy ball from K-Mart became a fiery ball of lava that had to be kept off the floor at all costs, chairs and chotchkes be damned—which seamlessly morphed into a two-on-one soccer contest with a laundry basket and the TV as goals. We got into a kind of fugue state, all worldly concerns slipping from our minds, a deep play that trendy folks in Beverly Hills would pay good money to induce.

Before bed, we hit the breakfast nook for a raid on available foodstuffs. While the boys silently fractured cold pop tarts into chalky shards, I ripped open a bag of beef jerky, pulled a piece apart to observe the hairlike filaments on the ruptured edge, gnawed hard on a hunk to release the exquisite burn of the extra spicy brand, felt the near terror, it was too much, it was too good. Before I knew it, I'd eaten the whole bag.

I could hear what my wife would say when she found the empty wrapper. "Let me guess, you ate it all," she'd say. My wife was repelled by my fierce appetites. I tried to explain that it was not about greed or gluttony. It was about experiencing life to the fullest. "It's about being a pig," she'd say. My hunger for women stemmed from a similar aspiration: to know humanity in all its infinite variations.

Boys abed, I curled up with Fogelson's *Fragmented Metropolis*, reading about why the LA basin had been an unlikely place to establish a big city—no natural port, no large river, subpar farmland. Apprehending the city's artificial, Oz-like quality, I drifted into a dream where all the city's buildings were made of pop tart materials, which if you walked on too heavily would collapse underfoot, dropping you into thick sand dunes. I woke to the sound of the party vibrating the pebbled sheetrock. Jody called to say she'd be a couple of hours late, and my fate was sealed. Jack and Teddy hadn't woken in the middle of the night in two years. I put on a nice shirt, leavened it with jeans and flip-flops.

My knock pushed the door open and from a smoky gathering Tiffany emerged like an apparition. She wore an old-fashioned party dress, sleeveless white chiffon dotted with cherries, playfully combined with ripped leggings, cowboy boots. People were strewn on every piece of furniture, a surprisingly pale bunch for LA, lots of torn T-shirts and asymmetrical haircuts—a mix of teenagers and twenty-somethings.

"Here Ray, I'll give you the tour." She led me through a human obstacle course to the liquor supply in the kitchen, which seemed to be it for the tour.

"Do you want something to eat?" she asked, sticking her head in the empty fridge.

"I'm fine, attend to your guests." She went to change the music and

I felt all eyes upon me, lone man fumbling to pour himself a Styrofoam cup of gin. By now, Teddy would have thrashed off his covers and swiveled around so his head was dangling off the foot of the bed, and Jack would be exactly as I left him, clutching stuffed koala, blanket wrapped tightly around him. Maybe this was a bad idea. In the hallway, I passed three guys with rooster hair talking about squatting in an unfinished condo.

"I applaud you fellows," I said. "Exercising your right to shelter, which should be enshrined in the constitution in a country as rich as ours." Tiffany reappeared and regaled them with the story of my ejection from the museum. Soon enough they were calling me dude, passing me a joint, treating me like someone younger than my years—a phenomenon I experienced fairly often, something about spending so much time with the boys that I acted and dressed like them.

Back in the kitchen for a drink, Tiffany asked, "Do you notice anything strange about this room, Ray?"

"You mean the earthy smell?" I asked.

"Exactly. God, everyone else thinks I'm crazy."

"We have it in our place, too," I said. "It's been driving me nuts."

"Ohmygod, don't you love this song?" She hugged me sloppily and I could feel she was revved up. Beneath her candyish perfume, I detected odd, complex odors, like something was off with her internal chemistry. She grabbed my hand and skipped us into a roiling cluster of rough-housing. From my ancient repertoire, I drew a dance called the pogo, which elicited amused exhortations from her clan. The music shifted to heart-thumping rap and the dancers seamlessly transitioned to hip-grinding. Tiffany pulled me to her, one arm in the air, the other around my lower back, and her pelvis slowly undulated, inviting mine to follow. When I was her age, it would have been a prelude to sex. But I glanced around and everyone was doing the same. At song's end, she held my head in her demi-gloved hands and pressed her lips softly against mine, her tongue darting coquettishly in my mouth. I felt a primordial male sense of conquest, simultaneously knowing I shouldn't be doing this.

"I just had to see what you tasted like," she said. Her eyes slid off to the side, and patting my arm, she ran toward an arriving trio of shaggy-haired fellows in hooded sweatshirts. Five minutes later, she was still occupied with them, so I staked out wall space next to a guy in parachute pants dancing privately to headphones. Tiffany beckoned one of the trio and reprised the hips-to-pelvis maneuver, and I disappointedly revisited my earlier assumption of conquest. As I reached for the door, a soft hand grabbed me.

"Come back soon," Tiffany said.

In the hallway I shivered with excitement and frustration. It reminded me of when I'd take a single bite of beef jerky and then hide the bag, to see how long I could endure the ache.

Nearing our apartment, I heard my wife coughing inside, and I thought "uh oh." But I remembered the building's balconies were attached. So I ducked back into Tiffany's place and elicited potsmoker applause by vaulting the four partitions that separated Tiffany's porch from mine.

I slid the glass door open, eased through the metal blinds, and there was my wife, trudging across the wall-to-wall with a bottle of Chardonnay and a coffee cup.

"Strange," she said, flopping on the couch. "I peeked out the window before and didn't see you."

"I've been sucking up the moist night air." I sat down next to her.

"Some wine?" she asked.

"Yes please. Can I get you a snack, there's that goat cheese you like." We went on like that, careful and polite, like people in mourning. I swept some recalcitrant hairs off her face, she smiled in a resigned way. Sometimes, at moments like that, late at night, when we were too tired to pick at the manifold sores we'd inflicted, it almost seemed as if our dreadful demise was something outside us, like a natural disaster we'd endured or a sad movie we'd seen, and we were huddled there in the aftermath trying to understand what we'd witnessed.

Jody laughed hoarsely. "What a bizarre arrangement we have here," she said.

"In our modern multicultural world," I said in the pedantic tone of a first-grade teacher, "there are all kinds of families. None is more right than the other."

Jody laughed again. How many years had I been doing that, trying to get a rise out of her. It was the dynamic we'd established: she was the practical, concrete one, I was the provocateur, the sensualist. It had begun when I was her history teacher at Cleveland State. I was older, an authority figure, so it took her longer than it should have to see through my bullshit. But once she did, she was relentless.

Jody patted my knee. "You know you're a really good father. They're lucky to have you." For a brief moment, all of my resentments evaporated, all those appetites for other women liquefied into a rush of guilt that tore at my stomach lining. I looked at her, those comfortable lips, those reassuring breasts, and wondered if after all that had transpired, it was possible to rescue things. Though maybe she had only complimented me to convince herself that she wasn't being used, that she was getting something in exchange for supporting my ass. And maybe I needed to feel there was still a chance of love between us so I wouldn't feel I'd stayed for the crass purpose of living off her dime.

During the subsequent week, as the boys and I motored around LA, my brain frequently rewound to that intimate moment at Tiffany's party. Did her desire to taste me represent a momentary impulse or a deeper hunger?

One foggy day as the boys and I played arcade games at the Santa Monica Pier alongside two-bit hustlers, I entertained the notion that Tiffany was one of those alluring and dangerous women you see in movies about LA, Faye Dunaway in *Chinatown* or Naomi Watts in *Mulholland Drive*. For a moment, I thought I spotted her amid the fog, leaning against the rail, enshrouded in a long black cape. But when the person faced me, it turned out to be a bearded magician in costume, deep-breathing to prepare for his act.

I thought, too, about my wife and our moment on the couch, her willingness, in spite of all my transgressions, to bless me with a compliment, the complicated flavor of a person like that.

In my distracted state, I tended to drive randomly. But this accorded well with the city's non-linear, associative logic. A cluster of high-rises would appear, oasis-like on the horizon, we'd drive toward it, discover, oh, that's Glendale, spot a surprisingly undeveloped mountain, drive over it, end up in something called La Cañada, see signs for a jet propulsion lab, get turned away at the gate by the guards, the boys diving down below window level, get on El Cerrito Boulevard to see where it led, find it led on forever, the addresses surpassing six digits, there's a Korean neighborhood, there's a Mexican one, there's a park constructed entirely atop an overpass.

From my academic training, I felt vestigial pressure to form a coherent analysis of Los Angeles. The problem was I'd always preferred the unpredictable zig-zag of gathering raw data to the careful construction of a logical argument. I hated being handcuffed to one intellectual framework—too much commitment. The boys could tell I was preoccupied.

"Daddy, what's wrong with your forehead?" Teddy asked, staring at me in the rearview mirror.

"Thinking about stuff," I said.

"You look sad."

"Just because I look serious doesn't mean I'm sad."

"I think a lot, too," he said. "But sometimes it makes me sad."

"Oh buddy, I'm sorry."

"It's cause you're sleeping on the couch and Mom yelled that time she didn't love you."

In the rearview, I saw Jack unlatch his seatbelt and slide over to his brother, hugging him as we continued along the blindingly white freeway.

Just when I was wondering when I'd see Tiffany again, I ran into her that afternoon near the elevator. She seemed morose and jittery, head down, devouring Doritos, face oily and pale. I couldn't believe this was the same girl who'd so dominated my thoughts. You didn't want to sleep with her—you wanted to hug and reassure her.

"The weird smell still affecting your place?" I asked.

"Yeah, it is. But I think I might have some relevant information." Her mouth clicked from dryness.

"Any clues are welcome."

"Like my buddies squatting in the Villandry wing? They stepped through the floor by accident and found some bones. They decided they were Indian bones and this place was built on top of an Indian burial ground."

"They've been watching too many B movies."

"I had a different theory. I thought since we're so near the tar pits they might be dinosaur remains. I even took a book out from the library." Her face, taut until then, flushed with excitement. I didn't have the heart to tell her the tar pits contained only mammals: sabertooths and mammoths.

The elevator doors opened, disgorging a middle-aged man with a briefcase and buzz cut.

"Hi Dad," Tiffany said. I was startled in the manner of someone who glances himself in a mirror and finds a jarring contrast to expectations. He was my age.

"Hello, I'm your neighbor," I said. "Your daughter and I were just discussing whether the La Brea Tar Pits might extend far enough to underlay this development."

"I'm glad someone can get her interested in science. I'm an aeronautical engineer and I've tried for years without success." There was a whiff of dying-breed sadness to this guy, with his short-sleeved white shirt, his pocket protector. He squinted at me with steely blue eyes and I sensed him sizing me up, probably reckoning I looked decent enough, more respectable than her anarchist friends, trying to give me the benefit of the doubt he'd want if he were chatting up a younger girl, if only he had the time to; he barely had time to keep track of his mercurial daughter. "Don't let me stop the discussion."

Tiffany, her face turning red, made a break for her apartment and her dad followed.

"Sorry," he said. "She can be kind of rude to strangers when her meds are off."

Tiffany's tar pit theory underscored a gap in my knowledge and by that evening I'd amassed a bracing assortment of new books, including JM Harris' *Treasures of the Tar Pits* (1985) and Merriam's classic *Fauna of the Tar Pits* (1911). But once I'd arranged them in a tidy pile, my interest flagged. I thought about my wife bivouacked in the master bedroom and decided to bring her milk and cookies.

"I already had dessert," she said, but grabbed an oatmeal raisin and coated it with a patina of milk. She wolfed it down and hugged herself. "This city's so hot and I'm always so damn cold."

"Do you want me to buy you a sweater at the mall?" I asked.

"Hey maybe we should have a date night some time," she said hopefully. Date night was a tradition from the early days when we'd go to a movie or show and then spend hours afterward dissecting it, Jody's intense focus and my insatiable curiosity an explosive mix. Our friends never understood why we found this tradition romantic.

"Great idea," I said, but inside I dreaded the daunting task of removing the crust from our fossilized marriage. I told Jody about our eldest comforting our youngest in the car. Suddenly, she was kissing me in that full-throttled way, grasping me in fierce holds.

"Sorry," she said, letting go. "I just needed to feel a man. It's been so long."

"I know what you mean," I said, going in for seconds.

"I don't believe it's been quite as long for you," she said, blocking me.

"If it's more apologies you need, I know I'm an asshole."

"Listen to you and yes you are. You'd go ahead and fuck right now, wouldn't you?"

"Well yeah. We are married."

"No matter that it's obviously an insane idea with all that's happened, that I'm going to need a lot more time to get over the idea you used to sleep with a married woman in our bed while the boys watched videos down the hall."

"That was only one time."

She shook her head. "You never really stop and think, do you, Mr. supposed scholar, you just follow along wherever things lead. You're like someone on these freeways, someone who sees a jam ahead and decides to merge onto a different freeway, even if that's not the way he was originally headed."

Feet pattered down the hallway and Teddy slammed into his mom's side.

"There were alligators," he stammered, gulping air.

"Hey Ray," Jody said after depositing Teddy in bed. "See if you can keep your paws off the girl down the hall, if this one time you can restrain yourself."

In the morning I stumbled outside in my boxers to get the paper and there was Tiffany, flanked by two flat-chested friends. Aside from her signature half-gloves, Tiffany had changed her style. All three girls sported short halter dresses in pastel shades, large designer sunglasses, lots of make-up, and expensive sandals.

"I think you forgot something," Tiffany said, smirking, referring to my lack of pants. I expected her to stop and talk, but she and her pals continued toward the elevator, whispering and giggling. I thought I heard one say, "He's so old." Clearly, Tiffany had no interest in having my paws on her today. I felt like I'd been humiliated in the school cafeteria.

To avoid stewing, I threw myself into boy play. I played anything my sons wanted, all those games I usually resisted because of their banality: rock-paper-scissors, Go Fish. I even gave in to their incessant pleas to visit a bland amusement park in the valley called Magic Mountain, though it boasted no historic value or distinctive features. It did give us the opportunity to drive home through the Inland Empire, a remarkable string of Spielbergian movie sets. When we stopped for gas, the attendant didn't even know what city he worked in.

"San Bernadino County, I know. But let me ask Irv."

The next day we hit the pool, planning to play Marco Polo. But Jack asked if we could just sit on the pool steps and talk—how cute was that.

"Dad, I like driving around, learning about cities," he said. "Can we do this in other cities, too?"

At that moment, Tiffany and Jamie came through the iron gate. She sat on the edge of the pool while the bro executed a magisterial cannonball that earned my sons' adulation.

"I was watching you from upstairs," she said, smiling sweetly.

"So you're a stalker?"

"You're so good with your boys." Color came into her freckled cheeks and she touched my wet wrist, as though my fatherly skill set had rendered me attractive once more. Again she'd surprised me: this girl was as protean as the hodgepodge city.

"They bring out the best in me," I said.

"You guys have such a nice positive energy. I could use some of that right now."

"Help yourself."

"Too many wasted nights with sinister people," she said. She had a chastened, regretful air. She stripped down to a tiny pink bikini and slid into the pool next to me and we did that grown-up thing I never understood as a kid, standing there not swimming, chatting away, slapping the water with our hands. It was gratifying to watch my simple stories about the boys fill her with the wholesome warmth she seemed to crave. I'd never seen her without her half-gloves and as she shooed Jamie toward the shallow end, I spied some ugly scars. She caught me staring at her wrists.

"It's not what you think. I used to cut myself is all. My doctor thinks it's because I was depressed." She smiled serenely. "It helps to tell you, actually."

"OK," I said. Teddy's lips were getting blue, so I needed to herd my guys toward a hot shower.

"You know we really should do playdates," Tiffany said as we parted.

That night, the boys tumbled around the floor, imitating the flopping Argentines in a soccer game on Fox Sports. Jody was out again, but then she called around 8 p.m. to say she'd be off in an hour and maybe we could do date night tonight, she had a work friend who could sit. This was Jody's version of an olive branch and I felt a surge of warmth. Then I heard someone struggling with our finicky nubbin of a doorbell.

"Hope we're not bothering you," Tiffany said. "We were kind of bored."

"Extremely bored," her brother said, darting past to join the soccer watching.

"Also," Tiffany said. "Like maybe this is a bad time, but there was something I wanted to show you. It might explain the smell." Tiffany was more carefully groomed than usual, sparkly eye shadow, spaghetti-strapped dress.

"What'd you find?"

"Just something in the basement."

"I'm alone with the boys."

"They look happy enough." They were motionless on the couch, a row of open-mouthed baby birds. I made sure the door was locked and Tiffany led me into the next wing, identical to ours except the plaster was unpainted and the doors lacked knobs. The elevator dinged open in the basement and we descended to the foot of the stairwell, reaching a dead end outfitted with a fire extinguisher and a fuse box. She said, "I found this oily pool down here one day and I thought it might be a tar pit."

"Intriguing," I said.

Under the stairs, the sheetrock was missing, and, stooping our heads, we stepped through the gap. We edged onto hard-packed dirt as Tiffany snapped on a bare bulb that revealed a vast unfinished basement forested with support beams. In front of us, near a cluster of mechanical equipment, was a puddle about ten feet across. I crouched beside it, dipped in a finger and pressed it to my tongue, detected a trace of petroleum. Plunging my arm to the elbow, I flinched at the squishy bottom sludge. There were hard chunks embedded in the sludge and I pulled one out and rinsed it. It was a small white arc the size of a pinkie, like a fragment of a sugar-coated pretzel, porous at each end.

"That looks like a bone, doesn't it?" Tiffany said with childlike exuberance.

"It kind of does," I said. I thought excitedly about all the new topics I'd have to investigate to assess this fragment—prehistoric bone densities, for instance, carbon dating, tar pit chemical composition.

"Do you think this is a tar pit?" Tiffany asked.

"It's always possible," I said. I had the momentary sensation that the whole summer had been leading to this moment. What a harmonious convergence: the chance to ingest new fields of knowledge while simultaneously encouraging this complex girl's inquisitive side. Suddenly, she leaped onto me and I was flattered by her assumption that I was strong enough to bear her weight. She nodded toward a metal door, and deciding our research could wait, I carried her toward it. The door led into the laundry room, where I gently placed her on a dryer. I could hear my wife's admonition: *keep your paws off her.* I knew I should try to restrain myself. But Tiffany grabbed my belt and pulled me between her legs and set upon me with that feverish tongue, and suddenly all I wanted was to thrust both hands up her dress, to touch every inch of her supple body, to inhale all of her at once. I caressed that irresistible young skin, what man can resist young skin, encountered some lacy grown-up underwear, slipped my finger beneath the waistband. Tiffany pulled at my shirt, yanked my hair, bit my chin.

"My friends thought I was crazy to like you," she said, pulling away. "My cousin and her friend, the girls you saw me with the other day in your boxers. They thought I should be grateful for the boyfriend I had. I was totally stoked with him at first—he's a skateboarder—I was celebrating with my bro's that first morning I saw you. But I'm tired of hanging with people my age. I want a boyfriend who can show me things."

I found the word "boyfriend" unsettling. In my previous affairs, there'd always been built-in limits—visiting professors who'd move away at the end of the semester, married women who had no intention of leaving their families.

"I think we might be getting ahead of ourselves," I said. But I couldn't resist kissing her again. She smelled so good, the sickly undertones from the first night were gone.

"No, but does that make sense to you, that we're right for each other?"

"How about we let our bodies get to know each other first." I nibbled her neck.

"I feel really clear about this. I think you're good for me, that positivity of yours, especially around your boys."

"There is a big age difference, we should give some thought to that," I said.

"It wasn't a problem for you the other night," she said.

"Maybe this isn't the best time to get into this, with the kids alone upstairs."

"Oh man this is such bullshit," she said, yanking her hands away from mine. "You're blowing me off. Here I am putting my heart out there and you're afraid to stray from your protected little world." I suddenly remembered my wife would be home soon.

"I need to get upstairs," I said.

Back in the condo, the boys stood in the middle of the living room rug, staring in horror at the K-Mart bouncy ball and pieces of a glass they'd apparently broken. Jody emerged from the kitchen with a dust pan and broom.

"Great work, Ray," she said. "I work 12-hour days and come home to *Lord of the Flies*." Tiffany picked up Jamie, tiptoed around the glass shards, and left the condo.

"I just stepped out for a second," I said. "I like that dress on you."

"Time to step out again." Jody pushed me into the hallway with the business end of the broom and slammed the door in my face. I caught up with Tiffany and Jamie as they entered their place and raced by them onto the balcony, to use it as a springboard. I climbed to our balcony and pulled on the door, but this time it was locked. I yanked on it several times, the blinds parted, and my wife's face appeared. She stared at me blankly and disappeared again. I realized she'd decided to lock me out for the night.

Some people, in particular my wife, would go crazy in a situation like that, having to wait so long with nothing to do. But it was a nice warm evening, and, after I settled into a chaise, I began to notice things that kept me occupied. For one thing, someone was moving into an apartment across the way. I could see an elderly woman in a wheelchair by the window, watching as three men in blue uniforms carried in boxes, struggled with a sofa, assembled a medical bed. I wondered what that was like, to move into one of these condos, knowing it was the last place you'd ever live.

At dawn, I jerked awake in a melancholy mood as a fog blanket inched over the rooftops. Before I knew it, doubts had invaded, causing me to second-guess my choices in the basement, to wonder if maybe I'd betrayed my commitment to tasting life's most potent flavors. Perhaps, I should have dug deeper, into the pool, into Tiffany's feelings for me. Fortunately, the multitudinous city sent forth something new to focus on. Above me, I spotted a bird trying to make a nest among the metal beams. Maybe,

I'd been still so long he didn't recognize me as a living being. He chose an unfortunate location, though, because the beams were only an inch wide, so most of the dirt and leaves fell uselessly onto the balcony floor.

An hour later, Jody slid open the door and stood with her arms crossed.

"You are a sick man. That girl is a child, Ray." Yesterday's blurred mascara brought out the loveliness in her brown eyes and I ached, recalling the hours I'd spent gazing into them.

"She's actually 20." I started to defend myself. "She's perfectly legal, number one, and number two, nothing really happened."

"What does 'nothing really' mean?" I spied the boys lurking at the edge of the living room and realized what I had to do. Silently, I went to the hallway closet, pulled a bunch of clothes from the shelves and threw them into a duffle, gathered my LA books from the coffee table, and headed for the door.

"Dad, what are you doing?" Jack yelled.

"Daddy, where are you going?" Teddy screamed. "Don't leave us, Daddy."

"Listen to your sons, Ray," Jody said. "You're not going to just rush out of here after the ruckus you caused, are you?" The boys latched onto my legs, but I shucked them off. It was for their own good. If I stayed, they'd have to endure their mom screaming at me for who knows how long.

I took up residence temporarily with Tiffany's anarchist friends in their squat in the unfinished wing. They hospitably offered to let me sleep on one of the chaises they'd pilfered from the pool area. They seemed excited by my presence until they discovered I was not my family's breadwinner and could not significantly augment the food/drug kitty. At which point they urged me to join them dumpster diving behind IHOP.

I assumed Jody would soon beg me to return, once she'd had time to feel the pinch of no child care. In the meantime, I made sure to call once a day on the basement pay phone that the anarchists had re-wired into a "freedom phone." Jody repeatedly insisted the boys didn't wish to speak to me. Eventually, I had to resort to good, old-fashioned epistolary communication, telling the boys about my hikes along the cement-lined banks of the LA River, dropping off my letters with the sweet-tempered Somalian college student who manned the guard house. In turn, he gave me my mail, such as it was.

One day there was a note from Tiffany that briefly lifted my spirits.

Dear Ray, she wrote. *Like hey yo. I'm writing because I just wanted to say I totally owe you a thank-you. You were so right to stop what we were doing in the basement that day. I don't know what I was thinking! I'd been skipping my medication and my head was totally effed up. I was partying like crazy, but when you said no, it was a wake-up call. My dad says if I stay clean, he'll talk to a guy he knows about me going to USC. I want to study archaeology. I'm taking good care of our bone, though my dad insists it's from a dog.*

The next day I received divorce papers, a major blow. I knew now the best I could hope for was partial custody. In my despair, I was tempted to blame Los Angeles—perhaps we'd been infected by its famous anomie. But the truth was, that whatever the future held, I would always have fond memories of our family's last summer together, of all the random exploration, of all the ways in which we'd learned from Los Angeles.

Another day, as I sat on my chaise, I heard little feet outside and two envelopes slid under the door. I threw on sweatpants, dodged fast-food Styrofoam, jumped gaps in the floorboards. "Jack, Teddy, come back, let's talk," I yelled as giggles trailed into the elevator. In the envelopes, I found letters on stationery from Petersen's Automotive Museum.

In his meticulous 4th grade printing, Jack wrote:

Dear Dad. Mom says you made a choice that you didn't want to live with us because you couldn't keep it in your pants and preferred a girlfriend who could be your daughter. I asked, didn't that mean she could be my sister, but she said no. I don't know why you didn't want to live with us. We never finished our laundry soccer game. I think I'm really mad at you for not baby-sitting right. So you probably should stop calling on the phone. I think maybe you are a fuckwad.

In a haphazard mix of upper and lower case, Teddy wrote:

Dear Dad. Mom says you left us alone so if there had been a fire we would not have been able to get out or an earthquake. Why did you want to be so mean?

When I finished reading, I realized it was over. Without the boys' support, I had no leverage. I knew family courts did not look kindly on unemployed men. I'd researched the major precedents.

If this were a movie, at this point I'd summon deep reserves of grit and determination, go out there and scrap for a respectable job to help me win the boys back. But I just can't imagine giving my life to a job that allowed no time for spontaneous adventure and intellectual investigation. I have survival needs, so I've secured a 25-hour-a-week position in a busy coffee shop near the downtown hotels. It pays for a little studio in a crumbling 20s building near the old Mexican market. I have sufficient room for a bed and my stack of current reading and a nice bright lamp, and it's a peaceful life in its way.

But I can't deny I have my dark moments. Sometimes, I'll be wrestling with a grey tub of crusty dishes and it'll hit me that perhaps I sacrificed my family for the chance at some heavy petting with a nubile but confused young girl. I'll close my eyes, trying to steady myself, and I'll flash on what Jody said about me always taking the less crowded freeway. I'll picture myself veering onto one of those enticing, uncluttered freeways, bursting out past the last vestiges of traffic, gunning the engine toward a gleaming plain of open road, and then realizing that the road seems to head endlessly downhill with no exit ramps in sight.

Eventually the moments pass, though. I'll remind myself that I helped steer Tiffany in a positive direction. And I'll imagine what a rush it'll be when I finally get to see the boys again. They'll no doubt have gotten bigger and developed new mannerisms and interests, but I'll have the schoolmaster's pleasure of searching beneath the new layers of growth for the residue of my influence.

CONTRIBUTORS NOTES

Lavonne J. Adams is the author of *Through the Glorieta Pass* (2007 Pearl Poetry Prize), and two award-winning chapbooks, *In the Shadow of the Mountain* and *Everyday Still Life*. She has published in the *Missouri Review*, *The Southern Poetry Review*, and *Poet Lore*.

William Archila lives in Los Angeles. His poems have been published in *The Georgia Review*, *AGNI*, *Poetry International*, *The Los Angeles Review*, *Notre Dame Review*, *Crab Orchard Review*, *Obsidian III*, *Rattle* and *Blue Mesa Review*. His first book, *The Art of Exile*, was published by Bilingual Press.

Jackie Bartley's poems have appeared most recently in *Nimrod*, *Southern Humanities Review*, and *sou'wester*. Her second poetry collection, *Ordinary Time*, won the 2006 Spire Press Poetry Prize.

E. Louise Beach is a teacher, translator, critic and poet. In 2009, her two song-cycles, *The White Princess* and *Ophelia's Flowers*, were performed in Birmingham, Alabama and at the Festival of Women in Music at the Eastman School in Rochester, New York.

Ellen Wade Beals is currently working on a novel and an anthology. Her poetry and fiction have been published in the *Willow Review*, *Willow Springs*, and *After Hours*.

Anemone Beaulier completed her MFA in Creative Writing at Georgia College & State University in 2007 and has published poems in *roger* and *The Cream City Review*. She lives in Macon, Georgia.

Peter Borrebach lives in Miami, Florida, where he is an MFA candidate in poetry at Florida International University.

M.L. Brown lives in Santa Barbara, where she devotes time to fundraising for a not-for-profit women's health care organization. Her poems have appeared in *Blackbird, Gertrude, Rattle, PoemMemoirStory, The Comstock Review, Birmingham Poetry Review, Ekphrasis,* and *The Chicago Quarterly Review.* She has an MFA from Antioch University Los Angeles.

Brad Buchanan teaches English at CSU Sacramento. He has published two books of poems and runs a small literary publishing operation called Roan Press. His work has appeared in *Canadian Literature, Fulcrum,* the *Journal of Modern Literature,* and *Twentieth Century Literature.*

Christopher Buckley's most recent book of poetry, *Modern History: Prose Poems 1987-2007,* is published by Tupelo Press, 2008. He was a Guggenheim Fellow in Poetry for 2007-2008 and teaches in the creative writing program at the University of California Riverside.

Mark Burke's work has appeared in *Poet Lore, Roanoke Review,* and *Hampden–Sydney Poetry Review.*

Jennifer Campbell is an English professor from Buffalo, New York, and a co-editor of *Earth's Daughters.* Her first collection, *Driving Straight Through,* was published in 2008 by FootHills. Her poetry has appeared in *Caesura, HeartLodge,* and *Nerve Cowboy* and is forthcoming in *Slant: a journal of poetry.*

Susana H. Case, professor at NYIT, has recent work in *Diner, Gulf Stream Magazine, Iron Horse Literary Review,* and *The Mochila Review.* She is the author of *The Scottish Café* (Slapering Hol Press, 2002) and *Anthropologist In Ohio* (Main Street Rag Publishing Company, 2005).

Crystal Charee is a creative writing student at Glendale College. Her poetry has previously appeared in *Eclipse*. She works as a register jockey at the local Goodwill.

Kevin Clark's book *Self-Portrait with Expletives* won the 2009 Pleiades Press contest. New Issues published his first, *In the Evening of No Warning*. Kevin's poems appear in the *Georgia Review, Iowa Review, Crazyhorse*, and *Gulf Coast*. Pearson Longman publishes his poetry writing textbook *The Mind's Eye*.

Douglas Collura lives in Manhattan. He is the author of a spoken word CD, *The Dare of the Quick World*, and a book, *Things I Can Fit My Whole Head Into*.

Jenny Yang Cropp is the author of a chapbook, *Hanging the Moon* (RockSaw Press, 2010). Her poems have appeared or are forthcoming in *Boxcar Poetry Review, Superstition Review, Hayden's Ferry Review*, and *Ecotone*. She received her MFA from Minnesota State University-Mankato and is currently working on a PhD in creative writing at the University of South Dakota.

Mary Crow has recently had poems accepted by or published in *A Public Space, Prairie Schooner, Interim, Verse, Wisconsin Review*, and *Field*. Her new collection of poems is *In Love with the Minotaur*.

Pam Crow lives in Portland, Oregon and works as a clinical social worker. Her poems have appeared in *Ploughshares, Southern Poetry Review*, and *Calyx*. Her work has been anthologized in *Of Frogs and Toads* and *The Bedford Introduction to Poetry*. Her first book, *Inside This House*, was published by Main Street Rag Press in 2007.

Lucille Lang Day's fiction and creative nonfiction have appeared in *The Hudson Review*, *Istanbul Literary Review*, and *Passages North*. Recipient of the 2009 Willow Review Award for Creative Nonfiction, she is also the author of many poetry collections and chapbooks, including *The Curvature of Blue* (Cervena Barva, 2009).

Tracy DeBrincat is an entertainment advertising consultant. Her first novel manuscript, *Every Porpoise Under Heaven*, received the 1996 Washington Award for Fiction. Her short stories and poetry have appeared in *Elixir*, *Karamu*, *Laurel Review*, *Madison Review*, *New South*, *North Dakota Quarterly*, *The Pinch*, *Primavera*, *Whiskey Island*, and *Zyzzyva*.

Karen Douglass's books include *Red Goddess Poems*; *Bones in the Chimney* (short fiction and poetry); *Green Rider, Thinking Horse* (non-fiction); and *Sostenuto* (poems). *The Great Hunger* (poems) is published by Plain View Press. She serves on the editorial staff *The Café Review*, a poetry quarterly.

Mary R. Estrada was born in Iowa. In her late teens she moved to Chicago. Ten years later, she lived in San Francisco for five years before moving to Los Angeles where she raised her two sons. She is currently a creative writing student at Glendale College.

Maria Fire, formerly a lawyer, hospice director, and massage therapist, has published a poetry and prose memoir, *Knit One, Haiku Too*. She lives in the mountains of Asheville, North Carolina.

Allen C. Fischer, former director of marketing for a corporation, brings to poetry a background in business. His poems have been published in *Atlanta Review*, *Indiana Review*, *The Laurel Review*, *Poetry*, *Prairie Schooner*, and previously in *Eclipse*.

Deborah Fleming has published poems in *ISLE, Organization & Environment, Karamu, Cottonwood, Natural Bridge, Hiram Poetry Review,* and *Tucumcari Literary Review.* Her chapbook *Migrations* was published by Finishing Line Press. She is editor of the Ashland Poetry Press.

Robert Funge's latest book, *The Passage,* was published in Ireland by Elo Press of Dublin, in 2001. Recent magazine publications include *The Chariton Review, Epoch, 5AM, New Letters, Pearl, Poetry East, Quarterly West, Rattle, Spillway,* and *The Wisconsin Review.*

Phillip Gardner is the author of *Someone To Crawl Back To,* a collection of short stories. Two collections, *Freaks Out* and *That Place Love Built,* are forthcoming. Gardner teaches at Francis Marion University and lives in Darlington, South Carolina.

Kenzie Gerr is a student at Glendale College whose career goal is to be a teacher.

David Gibbs is a graduate of the Ohio State University. His recent work can be found in the *Columbia Poetry Review* and *Mayday.* He lives in Columbus.

Maryfrances Gill, a native of Glendale and second generation student at Glendale College, is a previous contributor to *Eclipse.* She is currently writing the libretto, lyrics and music for an oratorio based on the life of Eleanor of Aquitaine.

Kathryn Good-Schiff received her MFA from Goddard College. Her poems have appeared in *Pank, Kalliope,* and *Quay.* She is an editorial assistant, leads writing workshops, and works in communications.

Kevin Griffith's book of poetry, *Denmark, Kangaroo, Orange*—a collection of prose poems—won the 2006 Pearl Poetry Prize and was published by Pearl Editions in 2008. His fiction has appeared previously in *Mid-American Review*. He teaches creative writing at Capital University in Columbus, Ohio.

Pierre Hauser's stories have been published in *The Iowa Review, BOMB, Confrontation, New South*, and *Quercus Review*. He won *BOMB*'s 2005 annual fiction prize. He is co-president of a foundation in New York and has degrees from Yale, Columbia, and the New School.

Richard Hedderman's poetry has appeared in *The Chautauqua Literary Journal, South Dakota Review, CutBank*, and *Puckerbrush Review*. He is the author of a collection of poetry, *The Discovery of Heaven* (Parallel Press, 2006). He lives in Milwaukee.

David Hovhannisyan was born in Yerevan, Armenia. He is a creative writing student at Glendale College and an introspective painter. His poetry has previously appeared in *Eclipse*.

Jean Howard has poetry published in *Harper's Magazine, The Chicago Tribune*, and her own book, *Dancing In Your Mother's Skin* (Tia Chucha Press). Currently, Jean serves on the Board of Slam Utah, Advisory Board of Utah Arts Alliance, and as a consultant for the National Poetry Slam Board, after serving as Director of Chicago's National Poetry Video Festival for eight years.

Marilyn Joy is a retired teacher of English and art. She is an active member of Oregon State Poetry Association and Willamette Writer's.

Ellen Chavez Kelley has received Academy of American Poets and Benjamin Saltman poetry awards. A past California Poet in the Schools and University of California lecturer, she teaches poetry, writes children's fiction, and tutors at Santa Barbara Community College. Ellen lives in Santa Barbara.

Sandra Kohler's second collection of poems, *The Ceremonies of Longing* (University of Pittsburgh Press, 2003) was winner of the 2002 AWP Award Series in Poetry. A first collection, *The Country of Women* (Calyx Books) appeared in 1995. Her work has appeared in *Prairie Schooner*, *The Colorado Review*, and *Beloit Poetry Journal*. After living in Pennsylvania for most of her adult life, she has recently moved to Boston, Massachusetts.

Anna Leahy's collection *Constituents of Matter* won the Wick Poetry Prize. She was a guest poetry editor for *Fifth Wednesday* and edited the collection *Power and Identity in the Creative Writing Classroom*. Leahy teaches in the MFA and BFA programs at Chapman University.

Barbara F. Lefcowitz's most recent poetry collection, *The Blue Train to America*, appeared in 2007. She has won writing fellowships and prizes from the National Endowment for the Arts, the National Endowment for the Humanities, and the Rockefeller Foundation. She lives in Bethesda, Maryland and is also a visual artist.

Joseph Levens lives in Smithtown, New York. His fiction has appeared in the *Florida Review* (2007 Editors' Award), *Sou'wester*, *Other Voices*, *New Orleans Review*, *AGNI*, *Meridian*, and *Swink*. He is editor of *The Summerset Review*.

Paul Lieber produces and hosts "Why Poetry" on KPFK radio in Los Angeles. His poems have been published in *Askew*, *Poemeleom*, *Spot Lit*, *Solo*, *Beyond the Valley of the Contemporary Poets*, *New York Quarterly*, *Santa Barbara Review*, and *Spillway*. He works as an actor on stage and in film and television. He lives in Venice, California.

George Looney's books include *The Precarious Rhetoric of Angels* (White Pine Press Poetry Prize), *Attendant Ghosts* (Cleveland State University Press), *Animals Housed in the Pleasure of Flesh* (Bluestem Award), and the novella *Hymn of Ash* (Elixir Press Fiction Chapbook Award). In addition, *Open Between Us*, a new book of poetry, is due out from the Turning Point imprint of WordTech Communications in 2010.

Joanne Lowery's poems have appeared in *Birmingham Poetry Review*, *Eclipse*, *Smartish Pace*, *Cimarron Review*, *Atlanta Review*, and *Poetry East*. Her most recollection is *Jack: A Beanstalk Life* from Snark Publishing. She lives in Michigan.

Chris McCarthy was Executive Vice President of Instructional Services at Glendale College from 1995–2002 before being selected as Napa Valley College's Superintendent/President later that year. For many summers he was proud to attend the Napa Valley Writers Conference and participate in both the fiction and poetry workshops. These are his first published poems.

Sarinea Meserkhani is a student at Glendale College and an aspiring interior designer. She was born in Toronto, Ontario, Canada, and is of four citizenships.

William P. O'Brien is a reformed technical writer who preferred the divine madness of poetry to the methodical madness of technical writing, but found that the latter enabled him to raise his family and further his education which, years later, he is still furthering.

Cully Pappas has lived in New York, Massachusetts and Georgia. She returned to Glendale College after 25 years to study creative writing. Her work has previously appeared in *Eclipse*.

J.J. Penna is a musician and poet residing in New Jersey. He received an MFA from Warren Wilson College in 2008 and has held fellowships at The MacDowell Colony, Atlantic Center for the Arts, and the Vermont Studio Center. Recent work is forthcoming in *Brilliant Corners, Fugue,* and *Nimrod.*

Justin Polikaitis was a poetry student at Glendale College who now lives in Australia.

Karen R. Porter resides in the Pinelands of South Jersey where she conducts conservation field work and tends to a large number of critters. She has recently appeared in *The MacGuffin, Water-Stone Review, Hawai'i Pacific Review,* and *Front Range Review.*

Marjorie Power lives in Corvallis, Oregon. Her most recent collection is *Flying on One Wing.*

Laura Powers is a graduate of the MFA program at the University of Idaho. Her most recent work appears in *Spoon River.*

Octavio Quintanilla's poems are forthcoming in *The Bitter Oleander, FUGUE, Santa Fe Literary Review, The Baltimore Review, Georgetown Review, Folio, The Fourth River, PALABRA, Weave Magazine, Existere: Journal of Arts and Literature,* and *The Mayo Review.* He is the assistant poetry editor for *American Literary Review.*

Zara Raab's poems and literary journalism have appeared in *Poetry Flash, Arts & Letters, North American Review,* and the *St. Louis-Post-Dispatch.* Her work is inspired by rural California. She studied at Mills College and the University of Michigan at Ann Arbor.

Charles Rafferty is the author of the poetry collections *The Man on the Tower* (Arkansas Poetry Award, University of Arkansas Press), *Where the Glories of April Lead* (Mitki/Mitki Press), *During the Beauty Shortage* (M2 Press), and most recently *A Less Fabulous Infinity* (Louisiana Literature Press).

Tera Vale Ragan is an MFA Creative Writing student at SFSU. She received her BA at USC, where she won the Virginia Middleton Award and Undergraduate Creative Writing Poetry Prize. She has traveled extensively from an early age and by crossing global borders strives toward crossing borders on the page.

Susan Richardson has work upcoming in *Broken Bridge, Rockhurst Review, The Dos Passos Review*, and *Argestes*. She works as the managing editor of Winterhawk Press and as a medical transcriptionist in Boise, Idaho.

Jack Ridl's new collection, *Losing Season*, is published by CavanKerry Press. *Broken Symmetry* (Wayne State University Press, 2006) was co-recipient of the best book of poetry award from The Society of Midland Authors. After teaching at Hope College for 38 years, he is now retired and soaking up the hours along the shore of Lake Michigan.

Judith Slater is the author of the story collection *The Baby Can Sing and Other Stories*, which won a Mary McCarthy Prize in Short Fiction and was published by Sarabande Books. Her stories have appeared in *Greensboro Review, Story Quarterly*, and *Ascent*. She teaches creative writing and literature at the University of Nebraska-Lincoln.

Talena Smith is a creative writing student at Glendale College.

S. James Stambaugh is a singer, songwriter, novelist, and writer of short prose. A native of Florida, he graduated from the University of Florida and currently resides in Hayesville, North Carolina.

Christine Hope Starr holds an MFA from Vermont College of Fine Arts. Her work appears in *Nebraska Poets on Sheldon Paintings* and is forthcoming in *Spoon River Poetry Review*. She mentors gifted writing students in the public schools.

Laura Stott received her MFA from Eastern Washington University. She teaches college freshmen and is an on-leave hiking guide and an ex-floral delivery driver. She currently divides her time between the small town of Skagway, Alaska, and Salt Lake City, Utah.

Diane Szabo was born in Cleveland, Ohio. She received a Master's Degree from Case Western Reserve University and attended the University of Pittsburgh, where she received a PhD in Germanic Languages and Literature in 1998. Her poetry has been previously published in *Flyway*.

Mark Taksa's poems appear in *Big Muddy*, *Karamu*, and *Margie*. Chapbooks include *The Biography Thief* (Pudding House), *The Future As An Act Of The Scissor* (Pudding House), *The Root* (Pavement Saw), *The End Of Soup Kitchens* (Pudding House), *Choice At The Blossom Café*, (March Street Press), *Cradlesong* (Pudding House), and *Truant Bather* (Berkeley Poets Workshop & Press).

Centa Theresa, poet and artist, has exhibited her mixed media pieces in galleries in the San Francisco Bay area. Her poems have appeared in *Drum Voices Revue, Sonoma Mandala, Tiny Lights, Women's Voices*, and *Writing For Our Lives*. Her collection of poetry, *Blameless Recognition of Natural Light*, was published by Clamshell Press.

Cammy Thomas' book of poems, *Cathedral of Wish* (Four Way Books), received the 2006 Norma Farber First Book Award from the Poetry Society of America. Her poems have appeared in *Agenda, Marlboro Review, 88*, and *Sahara*. She lives in Lexington, Massachusetts.

Carine Topal, a native New Yorker, writes and teaches in Los Angeles. Since 1982, she has anthologized the poetry of special needs children. She is the recipient of the 2007 Robert G. Cohn Prose Poetry Award. Her new collection of poems, *In the Heaven of Never Before*, was recently published by Moon Tide Press.

Benjamin J. Van de Griek was a poetry student at Glendale College who now attends UCLA.

Suellen Wedmore's work has been awarded first place in the Writer's Digest rhyming poem contest, and her chapbook *Deployed* was winner of the Grayson Books annual contest. After 24 years working as a speech therapist she retired to enter the MFA Program in Poetry at New England College, graduating in 2004.

Laura Madeline Wiseman is working on a dissertation at the University of Nebraska, Lincoln, where she teaches English. Her chapbook *My Imaginary* was published in 2009 by Dancing Girl Press. *Margie* and *Blackbird* have published her work.

Mark Wisniewski is the author of *One of Us One Night, Confessions of a Polish Used Car Salesman*, and *All Weekend with the Lights On*. His work has appeared in *Poetry, Poetry International*, and *New York Quarterly*, and he's won a Pushcart Prize.